Practice Book

A

The McGraw·Hill Companies

 Macmillan/McGraw-Hill

Published by Macmillan/McGraw-Hill, of McGraw-Hill Education, a division of The McGraw-Hill Companies, Inc., Two Penn Plaza, New York, New York 10121.

Printed in the United States of America

2 3 4 5 6 7 8 9 10 HES 13 12 11 10

Contents

About this Book

The pages in the Practice Book provide practice for skills and concepts taught in the program. At the start of the grade, children will need support to complete the pages. As children progress through the grade, they will be more able to complete the pages independently.

Start Smart

Activities in the Start Smart section are to be completed with assistance from the teacher. These pages are **"Read Together"** pages: pages you read to children and assist them to complete.

Units 1-3

Continue to read the direction lines to children and to model how to complete the activities. Depending on the individual children, the following pages may be done independently by children working alone or in pairs.

- Phonics
- High-Frequency Words/Vocabulary
- Fluency
- Structural Analysis

The following pages are **Read Together**:

- Concepts of Print
- Oral Vocabulary and Read Aloud/Listening Comprehension
- Text Features
- Literary Elements

Units 4-6

The **Read Together** pages in this part of the book are the Read Aloud/Listening Comprehension activities.

Start Smart

Contents

Unit 1 • All About Us

© Macmillan/McGraw-Hill

Contents

Unit 2 • Our Families, Our Neighbors

Contents

Unit 3 • Have Fun!

Contents

Unit 4 • Let's Team Up

Contents

Unit 5 • Nature Watch

© Macmillan/McGraw-Hill

Contents

Unit 6 • Adventures

Name _____

Say each picture name. Then write an **m** below the picture if its name begins like **map** or an **s** if its name begins like **sun**.

Write an **m** or **s** to complete the words.

_____ op

_____ ock

Name _____

Say each picture name. Then write a **p** below the picture if its name begins like **pin** or a **t** if its name begins like **turtle**.

_____

_____

_____

_____

_____

_____

_____

_____

_____

_____

_____

_____

Write a **p** or **t** to complete the words.

_____

_____ ig

_____

_____ ent

© Macmillan/McGraw-Hill

④

High-Frequency Words:
like, can, the, I, we

We can .

I like the .

①

I like the ⬚ .

③

We can ⬚ .

②

Name _____

Write a sentence. Use the letters from this page.

_____

- - - - - - - - - - - - - - - - - - - -

_____

Name _____

Say each picture name. Then write an **a** below the picture if its name begins with **a** as in **apple**.

Trace the word **at**. Then practice writing the word **at**.

Trace the word **an**. Then practice writing the word **an**.

Name _____

Say each picture name. Then write **c** below the picture if its name begins like **camel** or **n** if its name begins like **nest**.

_____
- - - - - - - - - -
_____

_____
- - - - - - - - - -
_____

_____
- - - - - - - - - -
_____

_____
- - - - - - - - - -
_____

_____
- - - - - - - - - -
_____

_____
- - - - - - - - - -
_____

Write an **a** to complete the words. Then read them.

- - - - - - - - - -
c ____ t   m ____ n
- - - - - - - - - -

- - - - - - - - - -
c ____ n   m ____ p
- - - - - - - - - -

Name _____

Write a sentence. Use the letters from this page.

_____

- -

_____

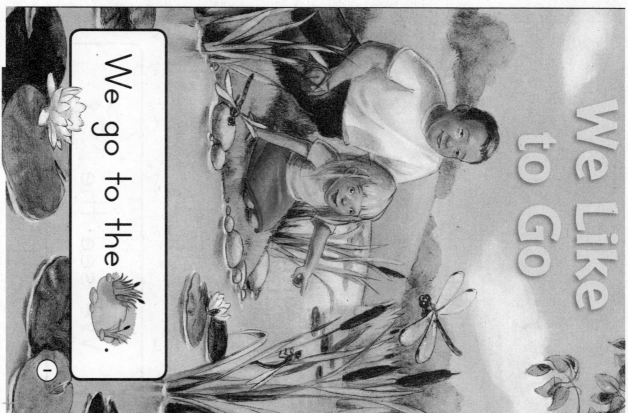

We Like to Go

We go to the .

1

We see the 🦀 .

High-Frequency Words:
we, go, to, the, see

4

We go to the .

③

We see the 🐸 .

②

Name _____

Say each picture name. Then write an **f** below the picture if its name begins like **fox** or an **h** if its name begins like **hat**.

_____

- - - - - - - - - - -

_____

_____

- - - - - - - - - - -

_____

_____

- - - - - - - - - - -

_____

_____

- - - - - - - - - - -

_____

_____

- - - - - - - - - - -

_____

_____

- - - - - - - - - - -

_____

Trace the word **if**. Then practice writing the word **if**.

_i_f_____

Write an **f** or **h** to complete the word.

_____
- - - - - - -
_____at

Name _____

Write a sentence. Use the letters from this page.

_____

_____

Name _____

Say each picture name. Then write an **i** below the picture if its name begins like **ink**.

_____
- - - - - - - - - - -
_____

_____
- - - - - - - - - - -
_____

_____
- - - - - - - - - - -
_____

_____
- - - - - - - - - - -
_____

_____
- - - - - - - - - - -
_____

_____
- - - - - - - - - - -
_____

Trace the word **in**. Then practice writing the word **in**.

Trace the word **it**. Then practice writing the word **it**.

Name _____

Say each picture name. Then write a **d** below the picture if its name begins like **door** or an **r** if its name begins like **rose**.

_ _ _ _ _ _ _ _ _ _ _ _   _ _ _ _ _ _ _ _ _ _ _ _   _ _ _ _ _ _ _ _ _ _ _ _

_ _ _ _ _ _ _ _ _ _ _ _   _ _ _ _ _ _ _ _ _ _ _ _   _ _ _ _ _ _ _ _ _ _ _ _

Write **r** to complete the words. Then read the words.

_____   _____

------------- at   ------------- an

_____   _____

Write **d** to complete the words. Then read the words.

_____   _____

------------- ad   ------------- id

_____   _____

We Have

I have a .

(1)

High-Frequency Words:
you, is, have

(4)

He is brown .

3 You have a .

2 He is .

Name _____

Write a sentence. Use the letters from this page.

_____

_____

Name _____

Say each picture name. Then write a **b** below the picture if its name begins like **bat** or an **l** if its name begins like **lemon**.

_____

- - - - - - - - - - - - - - -

_____

_____

- - - - - - - - - - - - - - -

_____

_____

- - - - - - - - - - - - - - -

_____

_____

- - - - - - - - - - - - - - -

_____

_____

- - - - - - - - - - - - - - -

_____

_____

- - - - - - - - - - - - - - -

_____

Write **b** or **l** to complete the words.

_____

- - - - - - -   all

_____

_____

- - - - - - -   ips

Name _____

Say each picture name. Then write an **o** below the picture if its name begins like **ox**.

_____
- - - - - - - - - - - - - -
_____

_____
- - - - - - - - - - - - - -
_____

_____
- - - - - - - - - - - - - -
_____

_____
- - - - - - - - - - - - - -
_____

_____
- - - - - - - - - - - - - -
_____

_____
- - - - - - - - - - - - - -
_____

Trace the word **on**. Then practice writing the word **on**.

_____

on -
_____

Write an **o** to complete the word.

_____
- - - - - - - - - - - - - -
_____ x

Name _____

Write a sentence. Use the letters from this page.

_____

_____

_____

© Macmillan/McGraw-Hill

We can play

High-Frequency Words:
she, he, said, play

④

He said, "I can

We can

①

We can play .

③

She said, "I can ."

②

Name _____

Say each picture name. Then write a **k** below the picture if its name begins like **king**.

_____

- - - - - - - - -

_____

_____

- - - - - - - - -

_____

_____

- - - - - - - - -

_____

Say each picture name. Then write **ck** below the picture if its name ends like **back**.

_____

- - - - - - - - -

_____

_____

- - - - - - - - -

_____

_____

- - - - - - - - -

_____

Use the letters **ck** to make new words.

_____

ki - - - - - - - - -

_____

si - - - - - - - - -

Use I letter to make new words.

_____

- - - - - - - - - **ick**

_____

- - - - - - - - - **ick**

Name _____

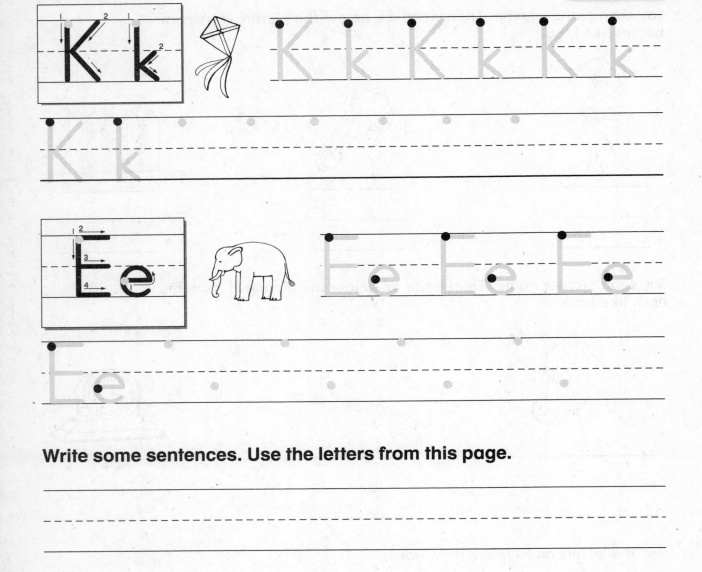

Write some sentences. Use the letters from this page.

Name _____

Say each picture name. Then write an **e** below the picture if its name begins like **egg**.

_____

- - - - - - - - - -

_____

_____

- - - - - - - - - -

_____

_____

- - - - - - - - - -

_____

_____

- - - - - - - - - -

_____

_____

- - - - - - - - - -

_____

_____

- - - - - - - - - -

_____

Trace the word **Ed**. Then, practice writing the word **Ed**.

Write an **e** to complete the word. Then read it.

_____

- - - - - - - - - -

_____gg

Name _____

Say each picture name. Then write a **g** below the picture if its name begins like **gate** or a **w** if its name begins like **web**.

_____
- - - - - - - - - - - - -
_____

_____
- - - - - - - - - - - - -
_____

_____
- - - - - - - - - - - - -
_____

_____
- - - - - - - - - - - - -
_____

_____
- - - - - - - - - - - - -
_____

_____
- - - - - - - - - - - - -
_____

Write **g**, **w**, **s**, or **b** to complete the words. Then read them.

_____
- - - - - - - et
_____
- - - - - - - et

_____
- - - - - - - et
_____
- - - - - - - et

We like the .

High-Frequency Words:
here, are, what, do, have, is, for

④

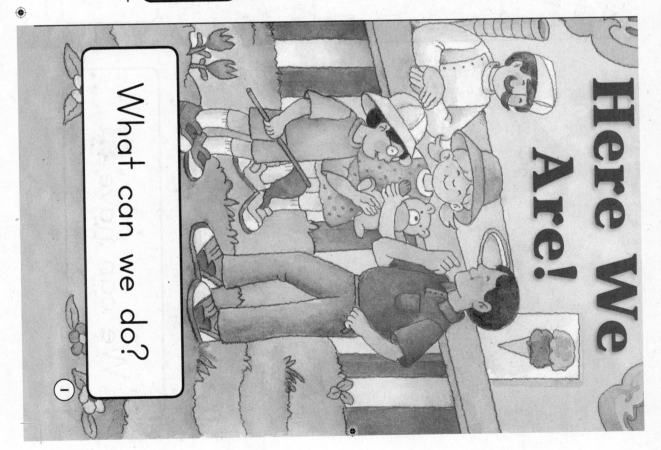

Here We Are!

What can we do?

①

We can have .

②

What is this for?

③

Name _____

Write a sentence. Use the letters from this page.

_____

_____

_____

Name _____

Say each picture name. Then write a **v** below the picture if its name begins like **van** or a **j** if its name begins like **jet**.

---------------   ---------------   ---------------

_____   _____   _____

Say each picture name. Then write an **x** below the picture if its name ends like **fox**.

---------------   ---------------   ---------------

_____   _____   _____

Write **v**, **j**, or **x** to complete the words. Then read them.

--------------- an   --------------- et

bo _____

Name _____

Say each picture name. Then write a **u** below the picture if its name begins like **up**.

_____   _____   _____

- - - - - - - - -   - - - - - - - - -   - - - - - - - - -

_____   _____   _____

_____   _____   _____

- - - - - - - - -   - - - - - - - - -   - - - - - - - - -

_____   _____   _____

Trace the word **up**. Then practice writing the word **up**.

_____

Trace the word **us**. Then practice writing the word **us**.

_____

Name _____

Write a sentence. Use the letters from this page.

_____

_____

_____

Look and See

Do you see my 🐶 .

①

She has a 🦴 .

④

High-Frequency Words:
do, my, look, is, was, has

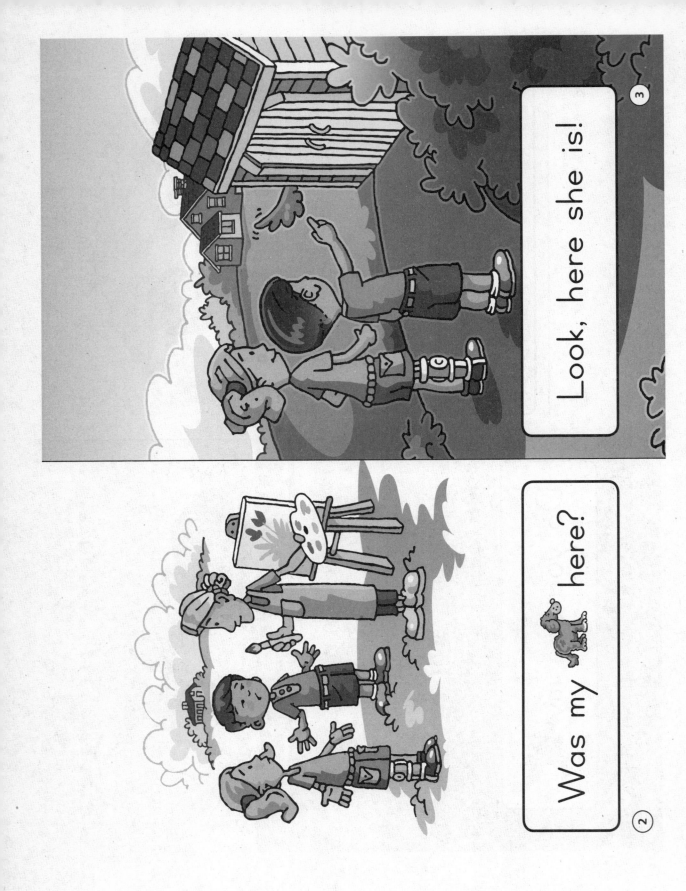

Look, here she is!

③

Was my 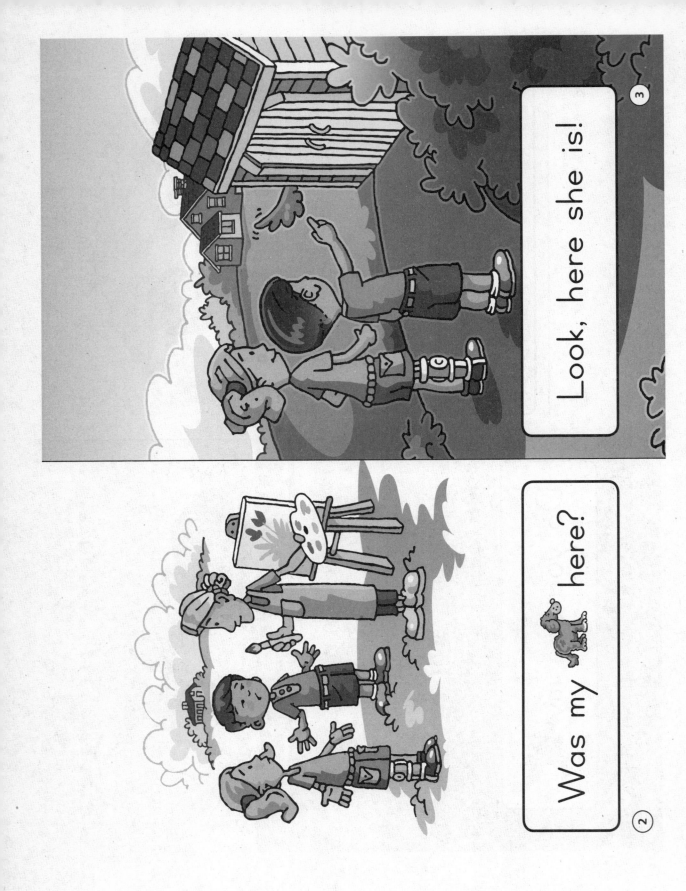 here?

②

Name _____

Say each picture name. Then write a **q** below the picture if its name
begins like **queen**, a **y** if it begins like **yarn**, and a **z** if it begins like **zoo**.

_____

- - - - - - - - - - - - -
_____

_____

- - - - - - - - - - - - -
_____

_____

- - - - - - - - - - - - -
_____

_____

- - - - - - - - - - - - -
_____

_____

- - - - - - - - - - - - -
_____

_____

- - - - - - - - - - - - -
_____

Write **q**, **y**, or **z** to complete the words.

_____
- - - - - - -
_____ ero

_____
- - - - - - -
_____ uilt

_____
- - - - - - -
_____ arn

Name _____

Write a sentence. Use the letters from this page.

Read the word. Circle the picture that it names.

1. cat

2. pan

3. man

4. sat

5. fan

Write a sentence using some of the words.
Check that your letters and words are in order left to right.

6. _____

_____

_____

Name _____

The Princess and the Pea is a fairy tale. A **fairy tale** is a story. It might tell about a king or a queen. It might tell about a prince or a princess. It might tell about magic, too.

Answer each question.

1. What do the words "Once upon a time" tell you? Circle your answer.

The story happened long ago.

The story happens today.

2. What happens first? Write your answer.

_____

- -

_____

3. The queen helps her son find a wife. How do you help someone? Draw or write your answer.

© Macmillan/McGraw-Hill

Name _____

Complete each sentence.
Use one of the words in the box.

up	not	jump

_____
- - - - - - - - - - - -
I. I can _____.

_____
- - - - - - - - - - - -
2. The cat ran _____.

_____
- - - - - - - - - - - -
3. The cat is _____ little.

Write your own sentence using a word from the box.
Check that you have left a space between words.

_____
- -
4. _____

_____
- -

_____

Name _____

Circle the word that names each picture.
Then write the word.

1.

cat   cats

_____

— — — — — — —

_____

2.

man   map

_____

— — — — — — —

_____

3.

pan   pans

_____

— — — — — — —

_____

4.

rats   rat

_____

— — — — — — —

_____

5.

mat   mats

_____

— — — — — — —

_____

6.

can   cans

_____

— — — — — — —

_____

7.

fans   fan

_____

— — — — — — —

_____

8.

hat   hats

_____

— — — — — — —

_____

As you read <u>Pam and Sam</u>, fill in the Character Chart. Use words from the story.

Pam Can	Sam Can

How does the Character Chart help you tell about the characters in <u>Pam and Sam</u>?

Name _____

Look at the pictures. Read the story.

Nat is a cat.
Nat can go up.
Nat can go down.
Pam and Sam look for Nat.
Pam is sad.
Where is Nat?

Write T if the sentence is true.
Write F if the sentence is false.

1. Nat is a cat. ____

2. Nat can go up and down. ____

3. Pam is not sad. ____

Write a sentence to answer the question.
Write capital and lowercase letters clearly left to right.

_____

4. Why is Pam sad?_____

_____

_____

Name _____

Look at the pictures. Write <u>1</u>, <u>2</u>, and <u>3</u> to show the order in which things happen.

A.

[ ]   [ ]   [ ]

B. Think about the pictures you labeled. Write a word that tells what is happening in the second picture.

_____

_____

C. Tell about something that you read this week.

_____

_____

Title _____

_____

Author _____

_____

What I Read About _____

_____

_____

Photographs are pictures that show people, animals, and things in real life.

Look at the picture.
Read the sentence that tells about the picture.

Look! My little cat is here.

Write your own sentence about the picture.
Check that your capital and lowercase letters are clear.

_____

- -

_____

- -

_____

© Macmillan/McGraw-Hill

As I read, I will pay attention to the intonation.

	Sam has a mat.
04	Can Pam?
06	Sam has a cap.
10	Can Pam?
12	Pam ran with the cap.
17	Pam can tap!
20	Tap, Pam, tap! 23

Comprehension Check

1. What does Sam have?

2. What can Pam do?

	Words Read	–	Number of Errors	=	Words Correct Score
First Read		–		=	
Second Read		–		=	

Name _____

Look at this story. Draw a box around the first word that you should read. Then point to each word as you read the story aloud.

Pat has a cat.
The cat can jump.
The cat can run.

Read the story aloud again.
Circle the capital letters.
Underline the lowercase letters.

Use the letters in the box to complete part of the alphabet. Make sure that the letters are in the right order.

a	G	c	h	F	e

_____   _____   _____

A _____   B b   C _____   D d   E _____

_____ f   _____ g   H _____   I i   J j

Name _____

Use the words from the box to name each picture.

| cat | hat | bat | pan | can | fan |

1. _____

2. _____

3. _____

4. _____

5. _____

6. _____

Name _____

> The Great Rope Tug is an African folktale. A **folktale** is an old story. Adults tell folktales to children. Some folktales teach something.

Answer each question.

1. What makes Rabbit mad? Write your answer.

_____

- -

_____

2. What words from the story name animals?
Circle the animals in this list.

rabbit	elephant	jump
Pam	over	hippo

3. How does the rope tug end? Draw or write your answer.

Fill in the sentences using the words in the box.

too	It	over

_____

- - - - - - - - - - - - - - -

1. _____ is in the
box.

2. You have fun,

_____

- - - - - - - - - - - - - - -

_____!

_____

- - - - - - - - - - - - - - -

3. It is _____ Pam.

Circle the word that completes each sentence. Then write the word on the line.

1. Sam _____.

      nap   naps

2. Sam and Pam _____.

      play   plays

3. Pam _____.

      pack   packs

4. Pam _____ go with Sam.

      can   cans

5. Pam _____ at Sam.

      look   looks

Name _____

As you read <u>I Can Too!</u>, fill in the Sequence Chart. Use words from the story.

First

↓

Next

↓

Last

How does the Sequence Chart help you retell the events at the beginning, middle, and end of <u>I Can Too!</u>?

Name _____

Look at the pictures.
Write <u>1</u>, <u>2</u>, and <u>3</u> for each column of pictures to
show the order in which things happen.

Name _____

Words that **rhyme** end with the same sound.
Rhythm is when words and sounds repeat to give
a poem a beat.

A. Circle the pictures that rhyme.

1.

2.

B. Read the poem.

Pat the cat
sat on a hat.

Pat the cat
sat on the mat.

3. Underline the words that repeat.

4. Write two words that rhyme.

_____

- -

_____

Name _____

> **Labels** give information about a picture.

Look at the picture. Read the labels.

hat

bat

cap

SAM

PAM

pack

Write the word that completes each sentence.

1. The man has a _____.

_____

2. Pam has a _____.

_____

3. The cat has a _____.

_____

4. Sam has a _____.

As I read, I will pay attention to pauses for sentence punctuation.

	Mack can jump up.
04	Mack can tag a pal.
09	Mack can bat.
12	Can Mack nap?
15	Mack can not! 18

Comprehension Check

1. What can Mack do?

2. Who could not nap?

	Words Read	–	Number of Errors	=	Words Correct Score
First Read		–		=	
Second Read		–		=	

Name _____

A. Identify the uppercase and lowercase letters.
   Point to each letter as you read it.
   Then draw a line to match each uppercase and
   lowercase letter.

d   e   r   g   o   k   l   b   w   i

L   D   B   R   W   I   G   E   O   K

B. Write the correct letter of the alphabet on the
   line. Write a lowercase letter.

1. c _____ e

2. m _____ o

3. p _____ r

4. j _____ l

Name _____

The letter **i** stands for the middle
sound in **big** and **fin**.

**Read the words in the box. Then write the word
that names each picture.**

pig	kick	pin	sit

1. _____

2. _____

3. _____

4. _____

**Write your own sentence using words from the box.
Check that your capital and lowercase letters are clear.**

5. _____

Name _____

**Write the word from the box that completes each
sentence. Circle the picture that goes with the sentence.**

be	ride	run

_____

- - - - - - - - - - - - - -

1. Nan will _____ here.

_____

- - - - - - - - - - - - - -

2. My cat can _____ here with me.

_____

- - - - - - - - - - - - - -

3. I can _____ with Nat.

**Write your own sentence. Use a word from the box.
Leave a space between the words in your sentence.**

_____

- -

_____

Name _____

Some words end in the same two consonants.

wi**ll**   ja**zz**   pa**ss**

Read each sentence.
Underline the word that ends with the same two
consonants. Write the word on the line.

1. Matt runs to his little cat.

_____

- - - - - - - - - - - - -

_____

2. Pam rides to the hill.

_____

- - - - - - - - - - - - -

_____

3. I kiss my Dad.

_____

- - - - - - - - - - - - -

_____

4. The mitt is on the ride.

_____

- - - - - - - - - - - - -

_____

Name _____

**As you read <u>How You Grew</u>, fill in the
Sequence Chart. Use words from the story.**

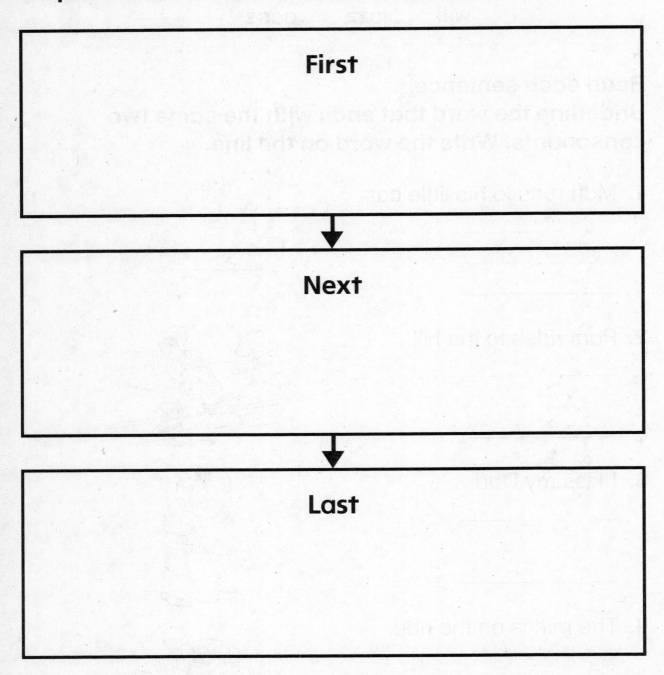

First

Next

Last

How does the Sequence Chart help you retell the order of
events in <u>How You Grew</u>?

© Macmillan/McGraw-Hill

Name _____

Look at the pictures.
Read the sentences.

 1. **2.** **3.** **4.**

The ball is down.
My cat and I play ball.
My cat runs down, too.
My cat plays with a ball.

Write the sentences in the correct order on the lines.

1. _____

_____

2. _____

_____

3. _____

_____

4. _____

Look at the pictures. Read the sentences.

The cat plays.

1.

Now the cat is big.

2.

The cat is little.

3.

Write the sentences in the correct order on the lines. Read them to retell the events.

_____

1. _____

2. _____

3. _____

Name _____

Nonfiction gives us information about real people, places, and things. When nonfiction authors tell about things that really happened, they put the events in order.

1. Look at the pictures. Write 1, 2, or 3 to show the order in which things happen.

2. How does the girl feel at the end of the story? Draw a face in the circle.

3. What is the girl doing?

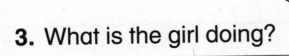
_____

_ _

_____

The **title** of a book is the name of the book.
The **author** of a book writes the story.
The **illustrator** makes the pictures.

Look at the book cover. Answer the questions.

1. Who wrote the book?

   _____

   - - - - - - - - - - - - - - - -

   _____

2. Who made the picture?

   _____

   - - - - - - - - - - - - - - - -

   _____

Title

Picture

Author

Illustrator

3. What is the title of the book?

   _____

   -

   _____

4. What picture is on the cover?

   _____

   -

   _____

Name _____

As I read, I will pay attention to the exclamation marks.

	"Can I hit, too?"
04	said Jim to Zack.
08	Jim is at bat.
12	Jim sits back as he hits!
18	Jim had a big, big rip.
24	Dad can fix it!
28	Jim has his bat back.
33	Jim did not quit!
37	"I hit it over!" said Jim.
43	"Yip! Yip! Yip!" said Tip. 48

Comprehension Check

1. What does Dad do?

2. What does Jim do?

	Words Read	–	Number of Errors	=	Words Correct Score
First Read		–		=	
Second Read		–		=	

Name _____

> Every sentence begins with a capital letter.
>
> Every sentence ends with a special mark.

Read this story aloud. Answer the questions.

I can sit.
I can run.
I am six.
Now I am big!

1. Draw a box around the first word you should read.

2. Find these words in the story. Draw a box around them.

3. Draw a circle around a capital letter at the beginning of a sentence.

_____

4. What letter follows the letter I in the alphabet? _____

5. Draw a line under an end mark at the end of a sentence.

Name _____

Blend the first two letters to read each word.

black   **cl**ap   **fl**ag   **cl**ip   **sl**ip

Use the words in the box to name each picture.

1. _____
   - - - - - - - - - - - - - - -
   _____

2. _____
   - - - - - - - - - - - - - - -
   _____

3. _____
   - - - - - - - - - - - - - - -
   _____

4. _____
   - - - - - - - - - - - - - - -
   _____

5. _____
   - - - - - - - - - - - - - - -
   _____

Name _____

Write the word from the box that completes each sentence. Circle the picture that goes with each sentence.

come	good	pull	down

_____

- - - - - - - - - - - - - -

1. It can _____ a cart.

_____

- - - - - - - - - - - - - -

2. It can swim _____ in the pond.

_____

- - - - - - - - - - - - - -

3. She will _____ if you call her.

_____

- - - - - - - - - - - - - -

4. He is _____ at sleeping.

Name _____

When **'s** is added to a word, it means that something belongs to that person or thing.

Circle the correct word and write it on the line.

1. This is _____ pet.

         Fran   Fran's

2. This is _____ bag.

         Gram's   Gram

3. This is the _____ trap.

         crab   crab's

4. This is _____ crib.

         Jim's   Jim

Write your own sentence. Use 's to show something belongs. Write your capital and lowercase letters clearly.

_____

_____

Name _____

As you read <u>Flip</u>, fill in the Plot Chart.

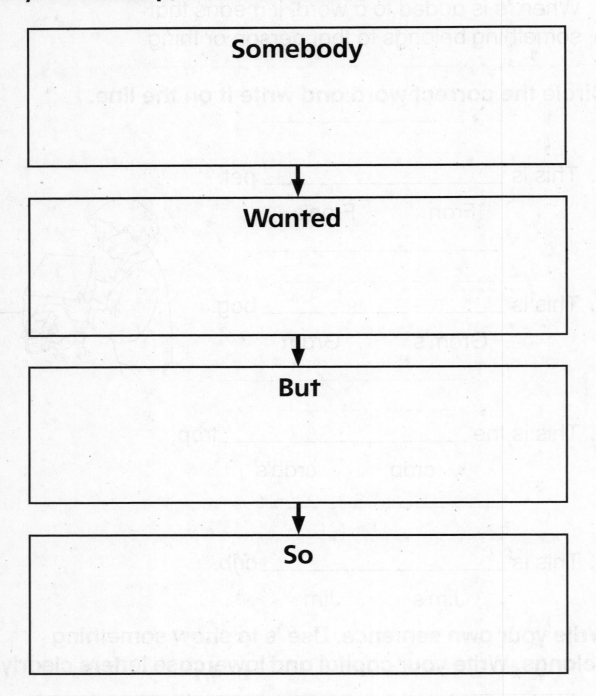

Somebody

Wanted

But

So

How does the Plot Chart help you better understand
the problem and solution in <u>Flip</u>?

Read the story.

The Baby Bunny

All the baby bunnies were sleeping in their nest. One baby woke up. He planned to have some fun. The bunny left the nest.

What a big place he saw! The bunny hopped and jumped. He had a good time. Then the rain fell. The baby bunny wished he was safe in his cozy nest.

Just then, he saw his mom. She was calling his name. The baby bunny hopped to his mom. They went back home. He was glad.

Read the sentences. Write <u>P</u> for the problem. Write <u>S</u> for the solution.

1. The rain came. _____

2. The bunny saw his mom. _____

3. The bunny wished he was in the nest. _____

4. The bunny went home. _____

A. Read the story.

Pip the big pig had a good day. His friend Pat the cat did, too. First, Pip sat in the sun. Pat sat in the sun, too. Pip took a nap. Pat did, too. Then Pip did six flips. Pat did six flips, too. Last, Pat took a ride on Pip's back.

B. Read the sentences. Write B for the beginning sentences, M for the middle sentences, and E for the end sentences.

1. Pip took a nap. _____

2. Pip sat in the sun. _____

3. Pat did six flips. _____

Nonfiction tells about real people, places, and things. Nonfiction may contain facts, dates, and names.

Read the sentences. Answer the questions.

Cats can jump.

Cats can nap.

Cats can run.

I. Write a word that tells what the sentences are about.

_____

_ _

_____

2. Write three words that tell facts about cats.

_____

_ _

_____

Name _____

> A **list** is a series of things written in order.

1. nap

2. sit up and beg

3. wag

4. play

Write two things from the list that pets can do.

_____
- -
_____
- -
_____

Name _____

As I read, I will pay attention to the exclamation marks.

	Sam is a clam.
04	Sam has a black back.
09	Sam can not run.
13	Sam can not ride.
17	Flip, flap, flip!
20	Sam can be big.
24	Flip, flap, slam!
27	Sam can be flat.
31	Clap, clap, clap!
34	Sam the Clam is glad. 39

Comprehension Check

1. What can Sam the Clam <u>not</u> do?

2. What does Sam do to be big and then flat?

	Words Read	−	Number of Errors	=	Words Correct Score
First Read		−		=	
Second Read		−		=	

A. Look at the story. Draw a box around the first word you should read. Read the story aloud.

I had a cat. It sat on Dad's cap.
I had a duck. It sat on Mom's mat.
I had a pig. It kicked Kit.
I got a bird. It is just right.

I. Find a capital letter in the story. Circle it.

2. Find these words in the story. Draw a line under them.

3. Add an end mark to this sentence.

_____

- - - - - - -

Sam is my cat _____

B. On the line, write the next letter in the alphabet. Write a lowercase letter.

_____   _____

- - - - - - -   - - - - - - -

4. f, g, _____   **5.** m, n, _____

Sometimes consonants form a **blend**. You can hear each consonant sound in a **final blend**.

ha**nd**   pa**st**

Say the word. Draw a line under the final blend.
Write the final blend on the line. Circle the picture.

_____
- - - - - -
1. a n t   _____

_____
- - - - - -
2. l i s t   _____

_____
- - - - - -
3. b a n d   _____

_____
- - - - - -
4. r i n k   _____

Roberto Clemente is a biography. A **biography** tells about someone's life.

Answer each question.

1. What sport did Roberto Clemente play? Write your answer.

   _____

   -

   _____

2. Tell about Roberto Clemente's life. Write 1 next to what happened first. Write 2 next to what happened later. Write 3 next to what happened last.

   _____ came to the United States

   _____ played with friends

   _____ helped children

3. Why was Roberto Clemente a hero? Draw or write your answer.

   ┌─────────────────────────────────────┐
   │   │
   │   │
   │   │
   │   │
   │   │
   │   │
   │   │
   └─────────────────────────────────────┘

© Macmillan/McGraw-Hill

Name _____

Use a word from the box to complete each sentence.

very	help	use	now

1. Tom can _____ Nan ride.

2. Look! What she did is _____ good.

3. Sam and Matt go up and down _____.

4. Dick and Nan _____ the big pot.

Name _____

A B C D E F G H I J K L M N O P Q R S T U V W X Y Z

The first letter of a word tells you where to put it in ABC order.

Read each set of words. Circle the word that comes last in ABC order.

1. miss   kick   ran

2. pass   go   hit

3. jump   over   run   fast

4. land   use   miss   go

5. pass   land   hit   over

Name _____

As you read <u>Soccer</u>, fill in the Author's Purpose Chart. Use words from the story.

Clue	Clue

↓ ↓

Author's Purpose

How does the Author's Purpose Chart help you understand the topic of the story <u>Soccer</u>?

Some authors write to tell a story. Some authors write to tell about real people or things.

**Read the sentences. Think about the topic.
Choose the author's purpose.**

1. Nan and I like to play soccer. Nan can run fast. Nan can run as fast as the wind. Can I pass her? Nan and I zig and zag on the grass. Nan can kick the ball up. I can kick it, too. But we can not use our hands. When the ball is out, we are sad. When it lands in, we are glad!

Author's purpose is:

○ tell a story about friends playing soccer

○ tell about real things

2. A band plays on the hill. Hank, Jim, and Dan play baseball. Nan, Pam, and I play soccer. Wag runs and jumps on the grass. Then it rains. Drip! Drip! Drip! The band packs up its van to go. We will play on another day.

Author's purpose is:

○ tell about how to play soccer

○ tell a story

> The **author's purpose** is why the author writes. Sometimes authors write to tell made-up stories. Sometimes authors write to tell facts about real people or things. The **topic** is what the text is mostly about.

Read the sentences.
Fill in the circle next to the correct answer.

1. Nat the ant helps Pat the pig pick six flowers. The author's purpose is to

   ○ tell a made-up story.

   ○ tell about real people or things.

2. Cats can sit. Cats can run. Cats can jump up and down. The author's purpose is to

   ○ tell a made-up story.

   ○ tell about real people or things.

3. It is Fish's birthday. Crab gives Fish a gift. Happy birthday, Fish! The topic of this passage is

   ○ Crab's busy day.

   ○ Fish's birthday.

Name _____

Words in a poem often **rhyme.** Rhyming words begin
with different sounds and end with the same sound.

m**ap**　　　t**ap**　　　cl**ap**　　　fl**ap**

**Read the poem. Write the rhyming words on the line.
Circle the same sound in each word.**

Where Did the Ball Go?

1. Pam can kick.
   Now she is very quick.

   _____

   -

   _____

2. Where will the ball land?
   Will it sink in the sand?

   _____

   -

   _____

Write words with / blends that rhyme.

Say your rhymes out loud.

_____

- -

_____

Name _____

As I read, I will pay attention to pauses for sentence punctuation.

	Fat Cat has a drum.
05	Fat Cat can hit it.
10	Pink Crab has a guitar.
15	Pink Crab can grab it.
20	Big Pig has a xylophone.
25	Big Pig can tap it.
30	Ant can help the band.
35	Pack Ant's van for the trip.
41	This is a jazz band!
46	Come and jig, jig, jig!
51	Ant taps and taps.
55	Ant jumps up and down.
60	Ant grins and claps.
64	The jazz band is good! 69

Comprehension Check

1. Who plays in the jazz band?

2. What can Ant do?

© Macmillan/McGraw-Hill

	Words Read	–	Number of Errors	=	Words Correct Score
First Read		–		=	
Second Read		–		=	

Name _____

Every sentence needs an end mark.

Sometimes the end mark is a period.

When you write a sentence, leave a space between your words.

A. Trace the capital letter at the beginning of each sentence. Then complete each sentence. Remember to leave space between your words. Include an end mark at the end of the sentence.

1. I ___ like to _____

2. A ___ t home, I help _____

3. M ___ y friend is _____

B. On the line, write the next letter in the alphabet. Write a capital letter.

4. J _____   5. C _____

Name _____

The letter **o** stands for the middle sound in **log**.

Blend the vowel and consonant sounds and say the word. Then write the word and circle the picture.

1. p o t _____

2. h o g _____

3. b o x _____

4. f o x _____

Write two sentences using these spelling words: hop, top, hot.

Check your spelling.

Name _____

Underline Wild Animal Families is **nonfiction**. Nonfiction tells about real people and things.

Answer each question.

1. What is <u>Wild Animal Families</u> mostly about?
   Write your answer.

   _____

   -

   _____

2. Tell about a wolf pup's life. Write 1 next to what happens first. Write 2 next to what happens later. Write 3 next to what happens last.

   _____ The pups get food from their parents.

   _____ New wolf pups cannot see or hear.

   _____ When they are six months old, wolf pups hunt with the pack.

3. How does a father penguin protect the egg?
   Write your answer.

   _____

   -

   _____

Name _____

Write the word that completes each sentence.

| Our | two | her | They |

_____

1. _____ cat is a mom.

2. The small cat naps with _____ mom.

3. This mom has _____ pups.

4. _____ play with mom.

Put the words on the top of the page in ABC order.
If the first letter is the same, use the second letter.

_____ _____ _____ _____

Name _____

> You can add **-ed** to some action words to tell what someone or something did.   **walk + ed = walked**

Circle the word that completes the sentence. Write the word. Then check your spelling.

_____

1. I _____ my bag.

   rocked   packed

2. Dad _____ the .

   locked   packed

3. Bob _____ up the dog.

   picked   licked

4. The cat _____ up on my lap.

   jumped   picked

5. Pat _____ the .

   rocked   kicked

Name _____

**As you read <u>Animal Moms and Dads</u>, fill in the
Main Idea and Details Chart. Use words from the story.**

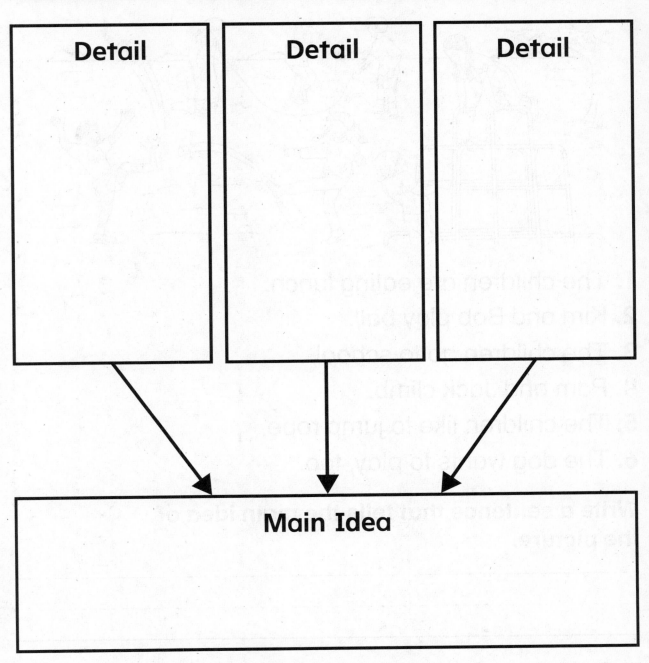

| Detail | Detail | Detail |

Main Idea

**How does the Main Idea and Details Chart help you
retell <u>Animal Moms and Dads?</u>**

© Macmillan/McGraw-Hill

Look at the picture. Circle all the sentences that tell important details about the picture.

1. The children are eating lunch.

2. Kim and Bob play ball.

3. The children go to school.

4. Pam and Jack climb.

5. The children like to jump rope.

6. The dog wants to play, too.

Write a sentence that tells the main idea of the picture.

_____

_____

_____

Read the passage. Then complete the items.

A puppy will be a dog. Its mom will help it grow.
A kitten will be a cat. Its mom will help it grow.
A tadpole will be a frog. Its mom will help it grow.

1. Circle the main idea of this passage.

Frogs like to sit in ponds.
Baby animals have a mom to help them grow.

2. Circle the group of pictures that shows the order in which the animals are talked about.

3. Circle what you think a chick's mom will do. Use details from the story to help you.

Go to the store.   Help it grow.

Practice

Literary Element:
Rhythm and
Rhyme

Name _____

Rhythm Poems are written so that the words have a certain beat when you say them aloud.

Rhyme Words that rhyme end in the same sounds.

Read the poem.

One little cat,
Sat on a mat.
She did not run,
She did not pat.

One little frog,
Sat on a log.
He did not jump,
He did not jog.

1. Write three words that rhyme in the first verse.

   _____   _____   _____

2. Write three words that rhyme in the second verse.

   _____   _____   _____

3. Say the poems out loud. Underline words that have a strong beat.

As I read, I will pay attention to patterns in the story.

	Mom Fox is very sad.
05	Where is Bob Fox now?
10	Is Bob Fox in Frog's pond?
16	Bob is not in Frog's pond.
22	Is Bob Fox in Tom's box?
28	Bob is not in Tom's box.
34	Mom Fox is sad.
38	Mom sits on a rock.
43	Mom can use help.
47	Ant can help Mom Fox.
52	Now Mom can see Bob Fox! 58

Comprehension Check

1. Why is Mom Fox sad?

2. Who helps Mom Fox?

	Words Read	–	Number of Errors	=	Words Correct Score
First Read		–		=	
Second Read		–		=	

A **sentence** always begins with a capital letter and ends with an end mark.

The end mark can be a period or a question mark.

Read this story aloud. Then complete the items.

> I like to dance. I am a star.
> I can sing. I am a star.
> I can jump rope. I am a star.
> I like to read. I am a star.
> What makes you a star?

I. Draw a box around the first word you read.

2. Find these words in the story. Circle them.

3. Underline a capital letter at the beginning of a sentence.

_____

_____

4. What letter follows that letter in the alphabet? _____

5. Circle the two end marks you see in the story.

© Macmillan/McGraw-Hill

Name _____

Use the words from the box to name each picture.

| pen | net | hen | leg | bed | ten |

1. _____

2. _____

3. _____

4. _____

5. **10** _____

6. _____

Write two sentences using these spelling words: men, let, get. Check your spelling.

_____

_____

_____

_____

Name _____

Write a word from the box to complete each sentence.

Who	some	of	No	eat

1. Did you get _____ for me?

2. _____ can get the down?

3. The bag _____ is in the box.

4. _____, I can not ride a .

5. Can I _____ with you?

© Macmillan/McGraw-Hill

Name _____

A **contraction** is a short form of two words. An **apostrophe (')** takes the place of the missing letters.   can + not = **can't**

| didn't | can't | doesn't | isn't |

A. Write the contractions.

_____

I. does not _____

2. did not _____

3. can not _____

4. is not _____

B. Write a sentence using a contraction from the box.

_____

_____

Name _____

As you read <u>Little Red Hen</u>, fill in the Retelling Chart. Use words from the story.

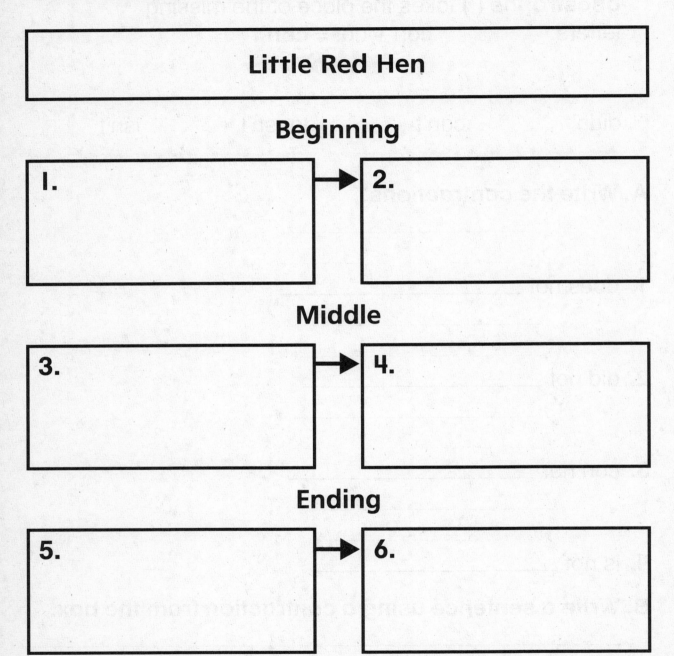

Little Red Hen

Beginning

1.

2.

Middle

3.

4.

Ending

5.

6.

How does the Retelling Chart help you remember the beginning, middle, and ending of <u>Little Red Hen</u>?

© Macmillan/McGraw-Hill

Name _____

When you **retell** a story, you tell what happened at the beginning, middle, and ending.

Read each story. Write a new sentence that tells the ending. Then draw a picture.

The red hen has two eggs.
She sits on the nest.
Now the eggs crack.
The chicks jump down from the nest.

_____

1. _____

Jen has a pet cat.
Greg has a pet dog.
Jen's cat jumps on Greg's dog.
The dog does not run.
Greg's dog licks Jen's cat.

_____

2. _____

Read the story. Then answer the questions.

I can get my mom a gift.
I will ask my dad for help.
I will pick the best gift.
I will tell my mom, "I love you!"

1. Look at the pictures. Write 1, 2, and 3 to show the order in which things happen in the story.

_____ _____ _____

2. The boy in the story has a problem. Fill in the circle that matches the boy's problem:

○ He needs help to get a gift.

○ He needs to run very fast.

3. Whom does the boy ask for help? Circle the picture.

A **folktale** is a story that has been told over and over again. Folktales often have talking animals that behave just as people do.

Think about a folktale such as "The Three Little Pigs." Many folktales have the same words at the beginning and the end of the story.

1. What do the words "Once upon a time" tell you? Fill in the circle.

   ○ The story happened long ago.

   ○ The story happened yesterday.

   ○ The story happens today.

2. What do the words "They lived happily ever after" tell you? Fill in the circle.

   ○ The story is about real animals.

   ○ The story is about real people.

   ○ The story is a folktale.

3. Think about "The Little Red Hen." Write what Cat, Pig, and Dog say when Hen asks for help.

   _____

   _____

   _____

Name _____

A **diagram** is a picture that shows the parts of something.

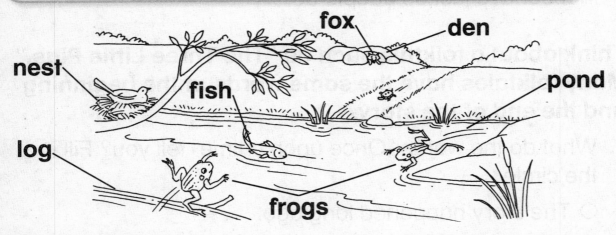

Write a word from the diagram to complete each sentence.

1. Two frogs jump in the _____.

2. The frog jumps off of the _____.

3. A fox is in a _____.

4. A _____ is in the pond.

As I read, I will pay attention to the questions in the passage and how they affect expression.

	"Ben, can Mom fix eggs?"
05	"Yes, Meg. Get two eggs."
10	"We have one egg.
14	Get Hen's egg, Ben."
18	Does Hen have eggs?
22	Ben is in her pen.
27	Hen is mad!
30	Meg yells for Mom and Dad.
36	They will help.
39	Splat!
40	Mom will not fix eggs.
45	Mom will fix ham! 49

Comprehension Check

1. Where does Ben go to get eggs?

2. Who does Meg get to help?

	Words Read	–	Number of Errors	=	Words Correct Score
First Read		–		=	
Second Read		–		=	

A **sentence** is a group of words that tells a whole idea. When you write a sentence, leave a space between your words. Include an end mark.

A. Circle the capital letter at the beginning of each sentence. Underline the first lowercase letter. Complete the sentence. Add an end mark.

I. My family helps me
_____

- -

_____

2. Who went to
_____

- -

_____

B. Write a sentence telling how you help at home. Check the space between words.

_____

- -

_____

- -

_____

© Macmillan/McGraw-Hill

Sometimes consonants form a **blend**. You can hear each consonant sound in a **consonant blend**.

Read the word. Write the word.
Circle the picture that it names.

1. g r a s s

   _____

   - - - - - - - - - - - - - -

   _____

2. c r a b

   _____

   - - - - - - - - - - - - - -

   _____

3. s n a p

   _____

   - - - - - - - - - - - - - -

   _____

4. c r i b

   _____

   - - - - - - - - - - - - - -

   _____

Write two sentences using these spelling words:
drip, spin, spill. Check your spelling.

Around Town, Then and Now is **nonfiction**.
Nonfiction tells about real people and events.

Complete each item.

1. How did people travel long ago? Write your answer.

   _____

   -

   _____

2. Tell about mail service long ago and today. Write 1 next
   to what happened first. Write 2 next to what happened
   later. Write 3 next to what happened last.

   _____ A stagecoach delivered the mail.

   _____ Mail is delivered by a mail carrier.

   _____ Pony Express riders delivered the mail.

3. How was school long ago different from today?
   Write your answer.

   _____

   -

   _____

Name _____

| live | many | out | place |

Write the word that completes each sentence.

1. Come to our _____ .

2. We _____ here.

3. We have _____ pals.

4. We go _____ to play.

Put the words on the top of the page in alphabetical order.

_____   _____   _____   _____

You can add **-ing** to some action words.

A. Add -ing to the words in the box.

look _____

jump _____

play _____

wash _____

B. Complete the sentences with the words you wrote. Check your spelling.

1. Beth is _____ a big dog.

2. They are _____ for a lost cat.

3. I am _____ with a little ship.

4. We are _____ up and down.

As you read <u>On the Map!</u>, fill in the Main Idea and Details Chart. Use words from the story.

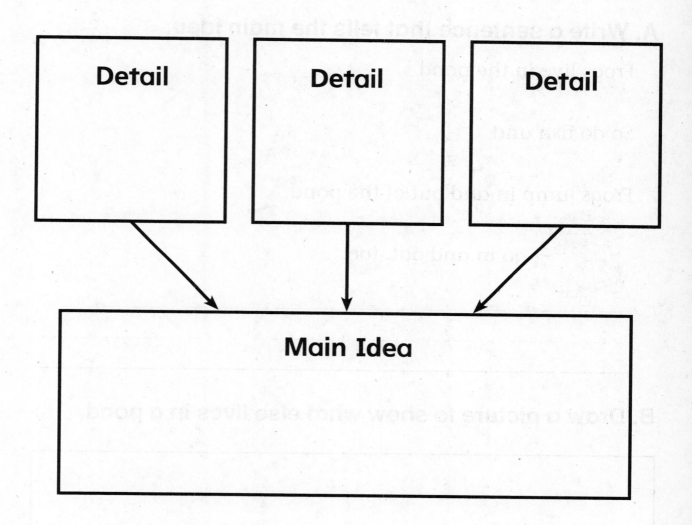

How does the information you wrote in this Main Idea and Details Chart help you retell <u>On the Map!</u>?

Name _____

Identify the **important facts and details** in a story.

Then state the **main idea**.

A. Write a sentence that tells the main idea.

Frogs live in the pond.

So do fish and .

Frogs jump in and out of the pond.

 go in and out, too.

_____

- -

_____

B. Draw a picture to show what else lives in a pond.

© Macmillan/McGraw-Hill

Name _____

Read the story. Then answer the questions.

I am a big black bear. I live in the woods.
Today it is hot. I stop to get a drink.
Now the leaves look red and yellow. It is not so hot. It is fall.
It is cold. It is snowy. I go to sleep.
I wake up. It is green and it is spring. I will eat a lot!

I. Look at the pictures below. Write 1, 2, 3, and 4 to show the order in which things happen in the story.

2. What is a good title for this story? Fill in the circle next to the best answer.

   ○ Bear Sees the Seasons

   ○ Bear Likes to Eat

3. Why will the bear eat a lot in spring? Fill in the circle next to the best answer.

   ○ He has been sleeping all winter.

   ○ A big apple fell next to him.

Name _____

A **dictionary** gives the meaning of words.

grand very big   **mend** to fix

ship a big   **lamb** a little

A. Write a dictionary word to complete each sentence.

_____

1. The _____ likes to run and play.

2. The ship is very _____.

3. I have to _____ my pants.

4. A _____ is too big for a pond.

B. Write a new sentence for one of the words.

5. _____

As I read, I will pay attention to questions in the passage and how they affect expression.

	Who can do a trick?
05	A lot of pets can!
10	Frizz has a trick.
14	Frizz can skip over a bat.
20	Ham can do some tricks.
25	Ham can run on a track.
31	Spot has a trick.
35	Spot can grab a rope.
40	Spot can spin.
43	Can Kit do a trick?
48	No, Kit can not.
52	But Kit can kiss.
56	It is a good trick! 61

Comprehension Check

I. What tricks can Frizz and Spot do?

2. What is the best pet trick?

	Words Read	–	Number of Errors	=	Words Correct Score
First Read		–		=	
Second Read		–		=	

A. Look at the story.
   Draw a box around the first word you should read.
   Point to each word as you read the story.

I am a cat.
I can jump up.
"No, cat!
Do not jump up!" said the man in the hat.
I ran fast!

B. Find these uppercase and lowercase letters in the story, and circle them:

m   s   p   D   I   t   a   N

C. Find these words in the story.
   Draw a line under each word.

Name _____

The letter **u** stands for the middle sound in **bus**.

Circle the word that names each picture.
Then write the word.

1.

   bun   big

   _____
   - - - - - - - -
   _____

2.

   pot   pup

   _____
   - - - - - - - -
   _____

3.

   ten   tub

   _____
   - - - - - - - -
   _____

4.

   sun   sad

   _____
   - - - - - - - -
   _____

5.

   bat   bug

   _____
   - - - - - - - -
   _____

6.

   drip   drum

   _____
   - - - - - - - -
   _____

Write two sentences using these spelling words:
run, fun, rug. Check your spelling.

Name _____

Write a word from the box to complete each sentence.

| could | again | one | make | Then | three |

1. I see _____ huts.

2. I like the red _____.

3. I _____ live in it.

4. _____ I can have two trees.

5. I will _____ a swing in one.

6. I will use it again and _____.

A **contraction** is a short form of two words.
An **apostrophe** (') takes the place of one or
more letters.

| he's | it's | let's | she's | that's |

**Read each sentence. Then write the contraction
for the underlined words.**

1. Mom said <u>she is</u> going with us. _____

2. <u>That is</u> a big truck! _____

3. <u>Let us</u> run and jump. _____

4. Ted said <u>he is</u> playing the drum. _____

5. <u>It is</u> a dull rug. _____

Name _____

As you read <u>The Pigs, the Wolf, and the Mud</u>, fill in
the Plot Chart. Use words from the story.

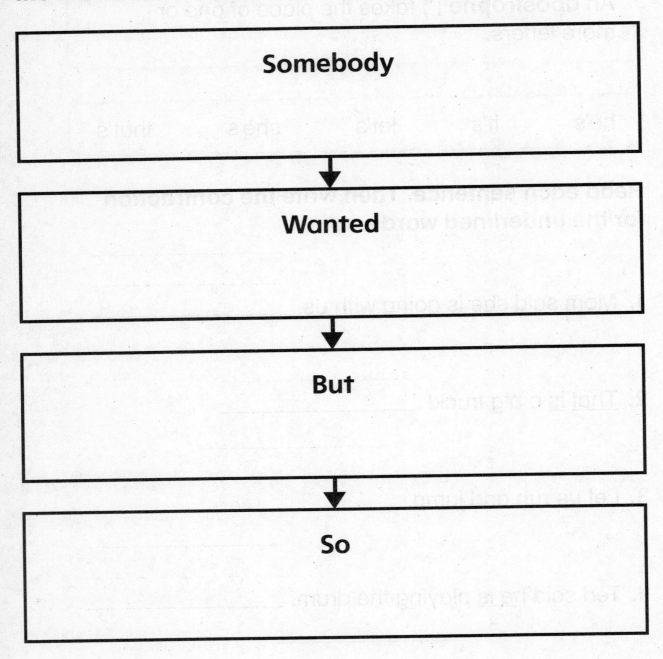

Somebody

Wanted

But

So

How does the Plot Chart help you better understand the
problem and solution in <u>The Pigs, the Wolf, and the Mud</u>?

Read the story.

Who Could It Be?

Meg lives in a small home. Bill lives in a small home, too. Meg and Bill play. They are pals. They like to ride bikes. They like to dress up. They like to play ball.

Meg's house is too small to play in. Bill's house is too small to play in. They go out to the yard. There is more room to play. Now they can play ball, ride bikes, and have fun together.

Read the sentences. Write <u>P</u> for the problem. Write <u>S</u> for the solution.

1. Meg and Bill have fun in class. _____

2. Meg and Bill live in small homes. _____

3. There is no room to play. _____

4. Meg and Bill play outside in the yard. _____

Name _____

> When you read, create a picture of the story in your mind. This will help you understand the story.

Read the story. Then answer the questions.

I like to run and jump in the mud.
I like to rub and scrub in the tub.
I get into bed. I am so snug.

1. Which picture shows what happens at the beginning of the story?

2. Which picture shows what happens in the middle of the story?

3. Which picture shows what happens at the end of the story?

© Macmillan/McGraw-Hill

A **folktale** is a story that has been retold for many years. Folktales are make-believe stories. Folktales are told all over the world.

Think about the story of "The Three Little Pigs."

1. What does the wolf always say to the pigs? Fill in the circle.

   ○ "May I please come in, little pigs?"

   ○ "Little Pig, Little Pig, let me come in!"

   ○ "Hello, pigs. Will you come to my house to play?"

2. What do the pigs always say to the wolf? Fill in the circle.

   ○ "Well, hello kind wolf! Won't you please come on in?"

   ○ "No, no, no! Go away and don't ever come back!"

   ○ "No, no, by the hair of my chinny chin chin. I will not let you in!"

3. Suppose that there is another little pig. That little pig tells the wolf, "No, no, by the hair of my chinny chin chin. I will not let you in!" What do you think the wolf would say next?

   ○ "O.K., friendly pig. I will go away and leave you alone."

   ○ "Then I'll huff, and I'll puff, and I'll blow your house down!"

   ○ "Please? I am a good wolf. I will not eat you!"

© Macmillan/McGraw-Hill

Name _____

> **Photographs** are pictures that show people,
> animals, and things in real life.

Look at the picture.

We will have a big place to live!

Write your own sentence about the picture.

_____

- -

_____

- -

_____

© Macmillan/McGraw-Hill

Name _____

As I read, I will pay attention to phrasing in the story.

	Gus and Fluff live in a fun place.
08	It has many nuts.
12	Gus and Fluff sit on nuts.
18	Gus and Fluff set nuts up.
24	Gus and Fluff eat nuts.
29	"Let us go out," said Gus.
35	"Yes," said Fluff.
38	"Let us get nuts!" 42

Comprehension Check

1. What do Gus have a lot of?

2. What do Gus and Fluff do with the nuts?

	Words Read	–	Number of Errors	=	Words Correct Score
First Read		–		=	
Second Read		–		=	

The **title** is the name of the book.

The **author** is the person who wrote the book.

The **illustrator** is the person who made the pictures.

A. Look at the book cover.
Answer the questions.

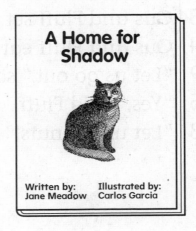

A Home for
Shadow

Written by: Illustrated by:
Jane Meadow   Carlos Garcia

I. What is the title of this book?

_____

- -

_____

- - - - - - - - - - - - - - - - - - -

2. Who wrote this book? _____

B. Complete this sentence about an animal's
home. Leave space between the words. Include
an end mark at the end of the sentence.

_____

- -

3. A frog lives _____

Read each word. Listen to the sounds that **sh**, **th**, and **ng** stand for.

pa**th**   **th**ink   **sh**ip   swi**ng**   di**sh**   ba**th**

Use the words in the box to name each picture. Then circle the letters that stand for the sounds <u>sh</u>, <u>th</u>, or <u>ng</u>.

1. _____

2. _____

3. _____

4. _____

5. _____

Write a word from the box to complete each sentence.

| all | want | under | Put | show | together |

_____

1. _____ on a hat.

_____

2. Sit _____ the tent.

_____

3. Come see the _____!

_____

4. The kids play in a band _____.

_____

5. You will _____ to see it.

_____

6. I like _____ the songs they play.

© Macmillan/McGraw-Hill

Name _____

A **compound word** is made up
of two small words.

rose + bush = **rosebush**

back + yard = **backyard**

**Match a word on the left to a word on the right to
make a compound word. Then write the word.**

1. bath   hill   _____

2. down   one   _____

3. any   care   _____

4. day   robe   _____

Use a compound word in a sentence.

5. _____

Name _____

As you read <u>Beth and the Band</u>, fill in the
Retelling Chart. Use words from the story.

Beth and the Band

Beginning

1.	→	2.

Middle

3.	→	4.

End

5.	→	6.

How does the Retelling Chart help you visualize what
happens in the beginning, middle, and end of <u>Beth and
the Band</u>?

© Macmillan/McGraw-Hill

Name _____

When you **retell** a story, you tell the beginning, middle, and ending.

Read the story.

Ben wants to use his fishing rod. Ben sits down at the pond with his fishing rod. Ben sits and sits. Ben sees a frog. Ben sees a bug. At last Ben gets a fish!

Draw three pictures to retell the story. Show the beginning, middle, and ending.

Name _____

Visualizing is forming pictures in your mind.
Visualizing helps you understand a story better.

Read the story.

I am not very big.

I have six legs.

I have three eyes.

I have two long tails.

I like to eat things that are red.

I live under a rock.

What do I look like? Draw a picture below.

Read the story again. Look at your picture. Fix things in your picture that do not match the story.

© Macmillan/McGraw-Hill

Name _____

> **Historical fiction** is a story set in the past. It is a story about something that did not really happen.

Long ago, a kind man lived by a river. He liked to bring treats to the fish. One night, the man could not sleep. He lit a candle. He went to the river to think. "I wish I could sleep," he said. As soon as he said this, a fish stuck its head up. The fish said, "You have left treats for me. I will help you." The fish sang until the man fell asleep.

1. What is the man's problem? Fill in the circle.

   ○ He can't find his candle.   ○ He can't sleep.

2. Write one word to describe the man.

   _____

   -

   _____

3. Retell the story. Write 1, 2, and 3 in the boxes to show the order in which things happen in the story.

   A fish sang the man to sleep. ☐

   The kind man took treats to the fish. ☐

   The man lit a candle. ☐

4. Write about a time you were kind to another person.

   _____

   -

   _____

Name _____

> **Directions** are the steps that you follow to make
> or do something.

Make a Fun Box

1. Get an egg carton.

2. Cut the top.

3. Give it a fun look.

4. Put in stuff.

_____

- -

1. What will you make? _____

_____

- -

2. What will you use? _____

_____

- -

3. What will you do with the top? _____

_____

- -

4. What will you do last? _____

Name _____

As I read, I will pay attention to the expression.

	Seth had a red can.
05	What could Seth make?
09	Thump, thump, thump!
12	Tim had a red lid.
17	Thud, thud, thud!
20	Beth had a flat dish.
25	Crash, crash, crash!
28	"Again!" Seth said.
31	One, two, three!
34	Thump, thud, crash!
37	Think of things to hit.
42	Then hit this and that.
47	Thump, thud, crash! 50

Comprehension Check

1. What sounds do Seth, Tim, and Beth make?

2. What do Seth, Tim, and Beth use to make sounds?

	Words Read	−	Number of Errors	=	Words Correct Score
First Read		−		=	
Second Read		−		=	

A. Read the story aloud. Complete the items.

I can do it. I will not quit.
I can pick six apples. I can run very fast.
I can jump. I did it!
Now I will make a pie. Yum!

1. Draw a box around the first word you read.

2. Find these letters in the story. Circle them.

c   I   q   N   p   a   Y

3. Find these words in the story. Draw a line under them.

B. On the line write the next letter in the alphabet. Write a lowercase letter.

_____   _____

4. d _____   **5.** h _____

Look at the word **gate**. The letters **a** and **e** stand for the **long a** sound you hear.

g **a** t e

Circle the word that names the picture. Write the word on the line.

1.

   cap   cape

   _____

   - - - - - - - - - - - -

   _____

2.

   tape   tap

   _____

   - - - - - - - - - - - -

   _____

3.

   pane   pan

   _____

   - - - - - - - - - - - -

   _____

4.

   man   mane

   _____

   - - - - - - - - - - - -

   _____

5.

   rat   rate

   _____

   - - - - - - - - - - - -

   _____

6.

   mate   mat

   _____

   - - - - - - - - - - - -

   _____

Read each sentence. Write a word from the box to complete the sentence.

away	school	today	way	Why

_____

– – – – – – – – – – – – – –

1. _____ did the bus go in the mud?

_____

– – – – – – – – – – – – – – –

2. This is the _____ to play.

_____

– – – – – – – – – – – – – – –

3. We put the blocks _____.

_____

– – – – – – – – – – – – – – –

4. I have to go to _____ now.

_____

– – – – – – – – – – – – – – –

5. We can not play _____.

Name _____

Look at the word: **wave**

Notice that the **e** is dropped when adding **-ing** or **-ed**.

wav**e** + **ing** = wav**ing**   wav**e** + **ed** = wav**ed**

Listen for the two syllables in <u>waving</u> and in some of the words you will make.

Add <u>-ing</u> to the words. Write the new word.

1. fake _____

2. rake _____

Add <u>-ed</u> to the words. Write the new word.

3. bake _____

4. fade _____

5. wade _____

**As you read <u>On My Way to School</u>, fill in the
Retelling Chart.**

1.

2.

3.

4.

How does the Retelling Chart help you remember the
beginning, middle, and end of <u>On My Way to School</u>?

Name _____

Look at the pictures. Write what happens in each picture.

1. First, _____
_____

Next, _____
_____

Last, _____
_____

2. First, _____
_____

Next, _____
_____

Last, _____
_____

In some stories the words **rhyme**. They have the
same end sound. Sometimes the words begin
with the same sound. This is called **alliteration**.

Read the rhyming story. Then complete the items.

I am a hen, and I say, "Cluck!"
I like to play with my friend, Duck.

Duck likes water, but I do not.
We both like the beaks that we've got!

We snap and snack on grass and bugs.
We like to share a lot of hugs.

I like Duck, and she likes me.
We live together happily.

1. Circle the words in the poem that rhyme.

2. Underline the word that begins the same way as *snap*.

3. Write to tell what you liked most about this rhyming story.

_____

- -

_____

_____

© Macmillan/McGraw-Hill

A rhyming story is like a poem. The rhyming words create a rhythm that makes the story fun to read.

I am not fast. I'm very slow.

I creep and crawl wherever I go.

I have a shell upon my back.

I eat some leaves if I want a snack.

I make a shiny, slimy trail.

Who am I? I am a _____.

1. Finish the story. Circle the picture that makes sense and rhymes.

2. Write a poem. Write about two things that you can see.

_____

_ _

_____

_ _

_____

A **sign** uses words or pictures to tell you what to do.

Circle the word that completes each sentence.

1. When you see , you _____.

                             stop   go

2. When you see , you _____.

                             stop   go

3. When we go to the , we play on the_____.

                       beds   swings

4. We _____ in the .

    run   eat

**Color the traffic light with red, yellow, and green.
Put a ✔ next to the color that tells you to go.
Put an X next to the color that tells you to stop.**

© Macmillan/McGraw-Hill

As I read, I will pay attention to my expression.

	We gave a pet show. It was
07	at the Tate School in Miss Hale's
14	class. Gale came with pet fish.
20	Shane came with his dog.
25	Dave came with a snake!
30	Jane came with a frog.
35	"His name is Wade," said Jane.
41	"Wade is the best pet."
46	"Why?" Gale asked.
49	Just then Wade jumped up.
54	Jane yelled, "Get Wade!"
58	We all helped together.
62	But Jane's frog got away!
67	Where did Wade end up?
72	He jumped in the fish tank! 78

Comprehension Check

I. What did Miss Hale's class do?

2. What did Wade do?

	Words Read	−	Number of Errors	=	Words Correct Score
First Read		−		=	
Second Read		−		=	

Name _____

The cover tells the **title**, or name, of the book. It tells the name of the **author**, or person who wrote the book. The cover also tells the **illustrator**, or person who made the pictures.

A. Look at the book cover. Then answer the questions.

1. Draw a circle around the title of the book.

2. Draw a box around the name of the author.

3. Underline the name of the illustrator.

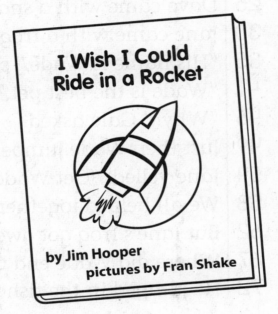

I Wish I Could Ride in a Rocket

by Jim Hooper
pictures by Fran Shake

B. Write two sentences about a book that you like. Check that you leave space between your words.

_____

- -

_____

_____

- -

_____

Name _____

Use the words in the box to complete the sentences.

| hike | time | five | bite | bike |

1. Matt races very fast on his _____.

2. What _____ is it?

3. I see the number _____.

4. Dan takes a big _____ of his cake.

5. We can _____ up this hill.

A **tale** is a story that has been told over and over again.

Think about <u>Now Things Are Worse</u>. Then complete each item.

1. How did Sam and Sara feel? Why?

_____

- -

_____

- -

_____

2. Circle the words in this list that tell what animals do.

bread   moo

cottage   bleat

cluck   bake

3. What was the wise man's final piece of advice? Draw or write your answer.

© Macmillan/McGraw-Hill

Use the words from the box to complete the story.

call	How	more	funny	There	so

_____

Look! _____ is a pet show today.

_____

I will _____ my dog Max.

_____ many pets will be in
the show today?

_____

Will they like Max _____
than the other pets in line?

_____

We like to watch some of the _____
dogs and cats.

_____

My dog Max is _____ good!

Name _____

The **c** in **cent** stands for the **/s/** sound. This is **soft c**.

The **g** in **gem** stands for the **/j/** sound. This is **soft g**.

The **dge** in **ledge** stands for the **/j/** sound. This is **soft g**.

Choose a word from the box to complete each sentence. Write it on the line. Then circle each word that has the soft c̲ sound.

race	fence	edge	cage
age	nice	stage	ice

1. This box has a sharp _____.

2. It is so _____ of you to help.

3. My pet mice are out of the _____!

4. I want to win the _____.

5. We will stand on the _____ to sing.

As you read <u>Smile, Mike!</u>, fill in the Predictions Chart.

What I Predict	What Happens

How does the Predictions Chart help you understand what happens in <u>Smile, Mike!</u>?

Read the sentences. Make a prediction. Read the words that tell what happens next. Check your prediction.

I. Tim's kite is ripped. Dad has some tape.

_____

I predict that _____

_____

_____

Dad fixed Tim's kite.

Was my prediction right? Circle: Yes No

2. Sam wants a nice pup. Mom and Sam go to see the pups.

_____

I predict that _____

_____

_____

Mom and Sam got a pup.

Was my prediction right? Circle: Yes No

Name _____

Read the story. Then complete the items.

I came home from school. My mom gave me a rake. I
wanted to play with Nate and Pam. I did not want to rake!
I raked and I raked, but the leaves kept falling! At last, I
had a big pile. Then Nate and Pam came to play.

1. How do you think the boy felt when he had to rake. Why?

_____

_____

_____

_____

2. Write 1, 2, and 3 to put the events of the story in order.

_____

_____ Mom gave me a rake.

_____

_____ Nate and Pam came over to play.

_____

_____ I raked and I raked.

3. What do you think the boy, Nate, and Pam will do next?

_____

_____

Read the chart.

Tim's Pets	Nan's Pets
cats 3	cat 2
mice 5	mice 2
dog 1	dogs 2
fish 9	fish 10

Count the pets and then complete the sentences.

_____

- - - - - - - - - - - -

1. Tim has _____ fish.

_____

- - - - - - - - - - - -

2. Nan has _____ mice.

_____

- - - - - - - - - - - -

3. Tim has _____ dog.

_____

- - - - - - - - - - - -

4. Nan has _____ fish.

As I read, I will pay attention to the expression.

	Mom and Dad rest today.
5	"Let's switch our jobs," Mike and Kim tell them.
14	"Fine," nod Mom and Dad.
19	"Would you like a snack?" Mike asks Dad.
27	Dad takes a bite. "This is not ripe! Take it away!"
38	Mom rides Kim's bike. "Your bike isn't my size,"
47	Mom tells Kim. "It is way too little!"
55	Dad must make Mike's bed.
60	"Let's make it line up," Dad tells Mike.
68	But Dad bumps the light.
73	Kim wipes up the suds. "I must rest," she whines.
83	"It's time to switch back," smiles Mom. 90

Comprehension Check

1. What does Mike do for Dad?

2. What does Kim want to do at the end of the story?

	Words Read	–	Number of Errors	=	Words Correct Score
First Read		–		=	
Second Read		–		=	

Name _____

A. Circle the uppercase letters. Underline the lowercase letters. Say the letters as you read them.

e	E	j	Y	z	W	v
V	y	G	g	J	Z	w

B. Follow the letters of the alphabet in the correct order to connect the dots and make a picture.

© Macmillan/McGraw-Hill

The letters **ch** and **tch** stand for the sounds you hear in **ch**in and di**tch**.

The letters **wh** stand for the sound you hear in **wh**en.

The letters **ph** stand for the sound you hear in gra**ph**.

Choose from the letters <u>ch</u>, <u>tch</u>, <u>wh</u>, and <u>ph</u> to complete each word. Write the letters on the line.

1. _____ ase

2. lun _____

3. _____ ale

4. _____ one

5. ca _____

6. al _____ abet

Match each sentence to the picture that it explains.

I. Is this **your** brush?

a.

2. Put the dolls **into** the box.

b.

3. The **people** sing the song.

c.

4. We will make a kite **soon**.

d.

5. Every sock has dots.

e.

6. The gift is **from** Mom.

f.

You can add **-s** or **-es** to name more than one person or thing.

Circle the word in each group that names more than one. Write it on the line.

1. watch   watches   what   _____

2. inches   pitch   inch   _____

3. such   lunch   lunches   _____

4. catch   patches   patch   _____

5. kisses   miss   kiss   _____

6. less   dresses   dress   _____

Name _____

As you read <u>Masks! Masks! Masks!</u>, fill in the Main Idea and Details Chart. Use words from the selection.

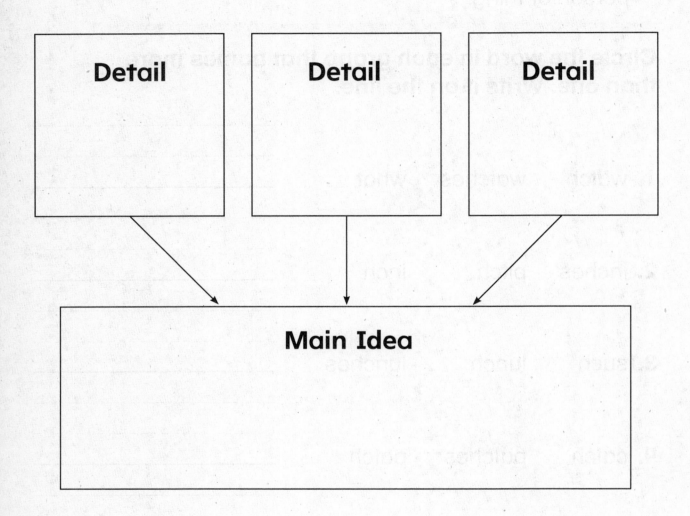

How does the information you wrote in this Main Idea and Details Chart help you retell <u>Masks! Masks! Masks!</u>?

Details are small pieces of information in a story.
The **main idea** is the most important idea in the story.

A. Read this story.

We went out.

We sat in the sun.

We ate lunch.

The sun went down.

It was a fun day!

B. Write <u>M</u> if the sentence tells the main idea.
   Write <u>D</u> if it tells a detail.

1. We sat in the sun. _____

2. The sun went down. _____

3. We ate lunch. _____

4. It was a fun day! _____

Name _____

Good readers think about the story as they read. If they do not understand something in the story, they go back and read it again. This is called rereading.

Read the story. Then answer the questions.

I get my brushes and paints.
I use red, white, and black.
I add more paint.
Soon people will come to my show.

1. What does "I use red, white, and black," mean? Reread the story to look for clues. Circle the picture that matches.

2. What kind of show do you think the story is talking about? Reread the story to look for clues.

_____

_____

3. What kind of art do you like to make?

_____

_____

Nonfiction tells about real people, places, or things. It gives facts and information. Think about the **main idea**, or what the text is mostly about, as you read. **Details** give you more information and help you find the main idea.

Read the passage. Then complete the items.

Dogs can be good pets.
You have to take care of them.
You must walk them every day.
You must give them food to eat.
You must play with them and love them a lot!

I. Underline two details in the passage.

2. What is the main idea of the passage?

_____

- -

_____

- -

_____

- -

_____

- -

_____

The **title** of a magazine is on the cover.
There are **articles** inside the magazine.

Use the <u>magazine cover</u> and <u>article</u> to answer the questions.

1. What is the title of the magazine?

_____

- -

_____

2. What is on the cover?

_____

- -

_____

3. What is the title of the article?

_____

- -

_____

4. What could the article be about?

_____

- -

_____

As I read, I will pay attention to question marks.

	The big sun is up at six.
7	People stretch in bed and then get up.
15	Let's check in with them.
20	Whip up a batch of buns.
26	I wish I had a hot baked bun. Yum!
35	Which one can I pick?
40	Kids can take care of a pet.
47	This dog gets some more fresh water.
54	When will the dog get fed?
60	Kids chat in a bunch. There is a lot to tell.
71	Did you make a graph in math? Don't be late for class!
83	Kids check the lunch case.
88	Munch on fish and chips! Grab grapes and a sandwich!
98	Play a game of chess. Pitch and catch a ball.
108	The sun sets in the west. I can see pink and red.
120	I had so much fun today! 126

Comprehension Check

1. When is the big sun up?

2. How does a kid take care of a dog?

	Words Read	–	Number of Errors	=	Words Correct Score
First Read		–		=	
Second Read		–		=	

Name _____

The cover tells the **title**, or name, of the book. It tells the name of the **author**, or person who wrote the book. The cover also tells the **illustrator**, or person who made the pictures.

Let's Make Art Together!

Written by: Pam Martinez   Illustrated by: Tim Underwood

A. Look at the cover. Then answer the questions.

1. What is the title of this book?

_____

_____

2. Why is Tim Underwood's name on the cover of the book?

_____

_____

B. Write two sentences about something that you have made. Check your spacing as you write.

_____

_____

Practice

Phonics:
Long *o*: *o_e*,
Long *u*: *u_e*,
Long *e*: *e_e*

Name _____

The letters **o_e** stand for the middle sound in **rope**.

The letters **u_e** stand for the middle sound in **cube**.

The letters **e_e** stand for the middle sound in **these**.

Read the word. Circle the picture that it names.

1. note

2. flute

3. eve

4. Write a sentence using some of the words.

_____

- -

_____

- -

_____

A. Write the word that completes each sentence.

| find | after | old | new |

1. Dad has _____ socks for

   _____

   Kim because hers are _____.

2. Can you help me _____ my glasses?

3. We go to the park _____ school.

B. Match the word to its meaning.

4. done   to do a job

5. work   finished

Name _____

In some words, the letter **k, g,** or **w** is silent. Some consonant digraphs contain a silent letter.

Meg **kn**its. A **gn**at is not big. I **wr**ap the gift.

Write the word from the box that fits each clue. In words with *kn*, *gn*, or *wr*, the letters *k*, *g*, and *w*, are silent.

gnat	knee	knapsack
write	knife	wrist

1. This is a kind of bug. _____

2. This body part is near your hand. _____

3. This is also called a backpack. _____

4. You do this with a pencil. _____

5. This is in the middle of your leg. _____

6. You use this to cut food. _____

As you read <u>Rose Robot Cleans Up</u>, fill in the Conclusion Charts.

Inference	**Inference**

Conclusion

. . . .

Inference	**Inference**

Conclusion

How do the Conclusion Charts help you better understand <u>Rose Robot Cleans Up</u>?

© Macmillan/McGraw-Hill

Name _____

> You can use what you read and what you already
> know to help you **draw conclusions**.

**Read each story. Draw a conclusion about the
characters' actions and feelings. Fill in the circle
of the sentence that makes the most sense.**

1. Jane bikes to school. She likes to
run races. She has fun jumping rope.
Jane plays ball with her pals, too.

   ○ Jane can do many activities
   because she is in good shape.

   ○ Jane can do many activities because
   she likes to take care of dogs.

2. Luke helps out at a home for older people.
He helps them walk. He tells them funny
jokes. It makes Luke feel happy.

   ○ Luke feels happy because he
   is like the older people.

   ○ Luke feels happy because he
   likes to help older people.

Good readers think about the story as they read. If they do not understand something in the story, they go back and read it again. This is called rereading.

Read the story. Then complete the items.

My name is Kate.
At school, we had to make old things into new things.
I used a box to make a pencil case.
When I was done, I put my pencils away.

1. Write a question that you would like to ask Kate about her pencil case.

   _____

   _____

   _____

2. Have you ever made something out of a box? What?

   _____

   _____

   _____

3. Where do you think Kate put her pencils? Reread the story to look for clues.

   _____

   _____

   _____

Name _____

> **Fiction** tells about something that is made-up. Sometimes the characters are animals that act like people.

Read the story. Then answer the questions.

I go to school with my pals.
The bell rings. We swim in.
Our teacher tells us to stay away from hooks and sharks.
We eat kelp for lunch. Then we swim.
On my way home, I see a big worm.
Then I see the hook and line. I swim past fast.

I. Who is the main character in the story? Circle the best picture.

2. Why does a fish go fast when it sees a worm on a hook?

_____

- -

_____

3. Think about what happened in this story. Tell a partner the story. Be sure to tell what happened in the beginning, the middle, and the end.

© Macmillan/McGraw-Hill

Name _____

A **floor plan** is a drawing that shows where things are in a room.

Use the floor plan to complete each sentence.

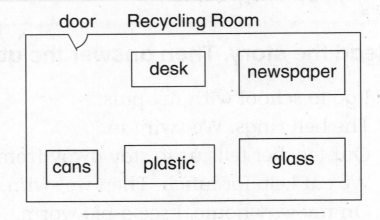

door   Recycling Room

desk	newspaper

cans	plastic	glass

1. The cans bin is next to the _____ bin.

2. If you can't tell which bin something goes in,

   _____

   ask for help at the _____.

3. Put ![bottles] in the _____ bin.

4. These ![newspapers] go in the _____ bin.

5. The smallest bin is for _____.

As I read, I will pay attention to the exclamation marks.

	"Can you give me a ride to an apple grove?" asked Mole.
12	"I can not," yelled Fox.
17	So Mole rode his bike.
22	"These nice apples are big and red," said Mole.
31	He chose ten, used a net and a pole, and then rode home.
44	At home, Mole lit his stove.
50	"I will make a pie," he said. "I will read and cut and mix.
64	Then I will bake."
68	"I hope it tastes good," Mole said with a smile.
78	"I will put on a robe.
84	Then I will take a nap."
90	Soon, Mole's nose woke him up. Mole ate every bit.
100	"What can I say?" Mole smiled. "It's just the best!" 110

Comprehension Check

1. Why does Mole need a net and a pole?

2. What kind of pie does Mole make?

	Words Read	−	Number of Errors	=	Words Correct Score
First Read		−		=	
Second Read		−		=	

A. Look at the story. Draw a box around the first word you should read. Point to each word as you read the story.

Some days I walk to school. Some days I run.

Some days I ride to school. That is fun.

Every day at school is the best day.

I learn and play. I help the teacher in every way.

B. Find these uppercase and lowercase letters in the story and circle them:

d   w   r   S   E   h   t   I

C. Find these words in the story. Draw a line under them.

Three letters can form a **blend**.
Listen for all three consonant sounds in each blend.

spring   **scr**atch   **spl**ash

Listen for the digraph and the consonant sounds in this blend.

throw

Write the new word on the line.
Connect the word to the matching picture.

1. scr + atch = _____

2. str + ipe = _____

3. spr + ing = _____

4. spl + it = _____

5. thr + ee = _____

> **Nonfiction** tells about real people and events. It gives facts and details about real things.

Think about <u>Schools Around the World</u>. Then answer each question.

1. How do children in China learn math?

_____

- -

_____

- -

_____

2. Tell about this article. Write 1 next to what you learned first. Write 2 next to what you learned later. Write 3 next to what you learned last.

_____ Kids in Cuba like to swing around a pole at recess.

_____ Kids who live in the desert in Egypt ride donkeys to school.

_____ Kids in the mountains of Ecuador wear hats to school.

3. Circle the words in this list that tell about schools.

picture   ride   books

teachers   recess   small

Match each sentence to the picture that it explains.

1. The **girl** can do lots of tricks.

 a.

2. The dog jumps into the **water**.

 b.

3. Will my **friend** drop the books?

 c.

4. **Does** the **boy** have fun with that rope?

 d.

5. The kids have fun **by** the lake.

 e.

6. Can you have **any** fun with a pet?

 f.

Name _____

When you add **-ed** or **-ing** to a word that ends with a vowel and a consonant, double the final consonant.

run + ing = ru**nn**ing   My dog is **running** fast.

chop + ed = cho**pp**ed   Sam **chopped** the log.

Read the sentence. Write the correct form of the word in the sentence.

_____

- - - - - - - - - - - - - - -

1. Mike is _____ the ball with a bat.

              hit

_____

- - - - - - - - - - - - - - -

2. The girl _____ the nice red mug.

              chip

_____

- - - - - - - - - - - - - - -

3. The kids are _____ the parts

              put

of the kite together.

_____

- - - - - - - - - - - - - - -

4. My dog just _____ over his dish.

              tip

Name _____

As you read <u>Kids Have Fun!</u>, fill in the Compare and Contrast Chart. Use words from the story.

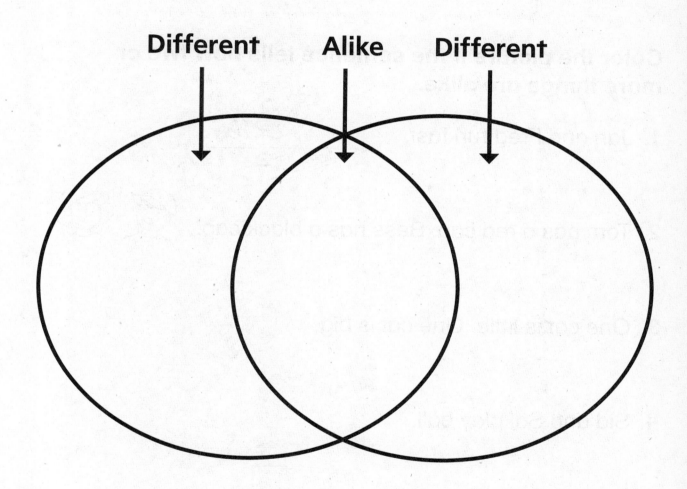

Different   **Alike**   **Different**

How does the Compare and Contrast Chart help you better understand the facts and details in <u>Kids Have Fun!</u>?

© Macmillan/McGraw-Hill

Name _____

When you **compare** two or more things, you tell how they are **alike**.

When you **contrast** two or more things, you tell how they are **different**.

Color the picture if the sentence tells how two or more things are alike.

1. Jan and Fred run fast.

2. Tom has a red cap. Bess has a black cap.

3. One cat is little. One cat is big.

4. Sid and Sal play ball.

5. All the kids go to school.

6. Both girls like to play.

© Macmillan/McGraw-Hill

Good readers think about the story as they read. If they do not understand something in the story, they go back and read it again. This is called rereading.

Read the story. Then answer the questions.

We have pen pals at school. Our teacher, Ms. White, helps us write to our pen pals. She sends the letters for us. Today, we got letters from our pen pals! They wrote that our letters made them feel happy. They said that they liked learning about other boys and girls. They hoped we could keep writing to them. That made us feel happy, too.

I. Do you think Ms. White's class will write more letters? Why? Reread the story to look for clues.

_____
- -
_____

2. Whom do you think Ms. White's class is writing to? Why? Reread the story to look for clues.

_____
- -
_____

3. To whom would you like to write a letter? Why?

_____
- -
_____

Writers use interesting and colorful words.
The **fluffy white** clouds float in the sky.

Circle the two words that a writer could use to describe each picture.

1. fast   soft   red

2. many   little   wet

3. black   one   hot

4. three   big   hot

5. little   many   big

6. hot   stink   yummy

As I read, I will pay attention to punctuation.

	I am Jon. I am six years old.
8	I am looking at photos.
13	I think it is so much fun.
20	Here I am with Mom and Dad.
27	Last spring, we went on a plane
34	to see Pop Streck.
38	I got a new knapsack!
42	This is Kim. Kim is five.
49	Kim has on a knit top. It has stripes and dots!
60	This big, black dog is Shag.
66	Shag made a splash in the mud.
73	After that, I had to scrub him and wring him out!
84	There is much more to see. But it is time for bed.
96	How can I save this spot? This string can save it! 107

Comprehension Check

1. What is Jon doing?

2. How are Jon and Kim different?

	Words Read	–	Number of Errors	=	Words Correct Score
First Read		–		=	
Second Read		–		=	

The cover tells the **title**, or name, of the book. It tells the name of the **author**, or person who wrote the book. The cover also tells the **illustrator**, or person who made the pictures.

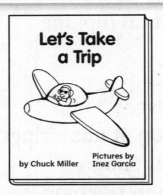

Let's Take
a Trip

by Chuck Miller   Pictures by
                         Inez Garcia

A. Look at the book cover. Then answer the questions.

1. What is the title of this book?

_____

- -

_____

2. Who is the author of this book?

_____

- -

_____

B. Write two sentences about a place that you would like to go. Check your spacing as you write.

_____

- -

_____

The letters **ay** and **ai** stand for the **long /a/** sound.

Jay
clay

Gail
sail

Use a word from the box to complete each sentence.

snail	pay	paint	clay

Ray

_____

1. Ray will use some _____ .

2. He will _____ the vase gray.

3. She will _____ for the tray.

4. A _____ is on the pail.

Write a word from the box to complete each sentence.

once	upon	carry	eight	across	saw	walked

1. _____ there were two chipmunks.

2. They _____ some nuts to eat.

3. The nuts were _____ the river.

4. The chipmunks wanted to _____ the nuts back.

5. They _____ on a log.

6. They put the nuts _____ their heads.

7. They made _____ trips.

Name _____

**As you read <u>Drakes Tail</u>, fill in the
Predictions Chart.**

What I Predict	What Happens

How does the Predictions Chart help you understand
what happens in <u>Drakes Tail</u>?

A **prediction** is a guess about what will happen next.

There is pizza on a plate. A good **prediction** would be that someone will eat the pizza.

Draw a line connecting each sentence with the one that tells what will happen next.

1. The block falls down.   Tim will pick it up.

2. The frog sees a pond.   The vet will help.

3. A dog is sick.   It will hop in.

4. Dad gets a cake.   She will run fast.

5. Jan gets a doll.   She will play with it.

6. Peg is late for school.   He will eat it.

Make your own prediction.

7. Jake has a gift from his friend Meg.

_____

- -

_____

Good readers ask questions about the story as they read. If something is not clear go back and reread to answer your questions.

Read the story. Then answer the questions.

Today is field day at school. We pick teams. Tom is the smallest boy. Will anyone pick him? He is the last one picked. First, we have a relay race. Tom is not the fastest, but he tries to help the team. Then, we have to race to carry one of our teammates across the field. Tom is the lightest. Our team wins! Hooray for Tom!

I. How do you think Tom feels when he is the last one picked?

_____

_____

2. Write a question you have about the story.

_____

_____

3. Reread the story to look for clues to answer your question. Write an answer to your question.

_____

_____

You can add **-er** or **-est** to compare two or more persons or things. The ending **-er** can mean "more." The ending **-est** can mean "most." Listen for the two sounds in **older** and **oldest** and in some of the other words ending in **-er** and **-est**.

A. Circle the word in each group that names something that is more than another thing.

1.	fast	faster	fastest
2.	newer	new	newest
3.	dark	darkest	darker

B. Circle the word in each group that names something that is the most.

4.	cold	coldest	colder
5.	soon	sooner	soonest
6.	small	smaller	smallest

A **dictionary** is a book that gives the meaning of words. Some words have more than one meaning.

Read the definitions below.

bark 1. the outside cover of a tree: The **bark** on the tree fell off. **2.** to make the sound that a dog makes: His dog will **bark** at all cats.

seal 1. an animal that lives in the ocean most of the time and swims very well: The **seal** swam over the wave. **2.** to close something so that it can not be opened: I had to **seal** the box with tape to close it.

Choose the correct definition for the word.
Fill in the circle.

1. bark ○ drop a pole ○ sound like a dog

2. bark ○ part of a tree ○ in a pot

3. seal ○ run away ○ close a box very well

4. seal ○ a blue ship ○ an animal that swims

Use a word from above in a sentence.

_____

- -

_____

Name _____

As I read, I will pay attention to my expression.

	Rain is on Mom's gray rug. Rain is in Mom's braid.
11	Rain is on Big Jay's tail.
17	There is so much water!
22	I get any pails I can find. I help Mom.
32	I catch a lot of rain.
38	The rain has stopped. May I run and play?
47	This yard has too much mud! Big Jay can't
	use his house.
59	Big Jay sits and waits.
64	I see a big rainbow! It makes us smile.
73	It's a fine day after all! 79

Comprehension Check

1. What does the rain get on?

2. Why can't Big Jay use his house?

	Words Read	−	Number of Errors	=	Words Correct Score
First Read		−		=	
Second Read		−		=	

A **song** has words called **lyrics** that are sung to music. The words have a **rhythm** and can **rhyme**. Many songs have a **chorus**, or lines that repeat. **Alliteration** is the same beginning sound in words.

Think about the song "Aiken Drum." Then answer the questions.

1. Work with a partner. Tell the words that repeat in "Aiken Drum." Take turns saying them aloud.

2. Say the first line of the song. Write the words that show alliteration. Circle the letters that stand for the beginning sound that is repeated.

_____

- -

_____

3. Write a short poem about things you hear or see every day. Use words that rhyme, words that repeat, or words with the same beginning sounds if you wish. Make up a tune for your poem. Sing your song to a partner.

_____

- -

_____

- -

_____

> **Captions** tell readers more about a photograph or picture.

Circle the caption that tells about the picture.

1. a snake
a baby deer

2. Big Bass Lake
the waterslide

3. my new bike
Big Buck Forest

4. the swimming pool
the campfire

5. our campsite
last day of school

6. Dad's big catch!
Sam's new dog

Name _____

A **Reading Log** tells about something that you read.

Read a fiction book or a nonfiction book every day this week. Then tell about what you read.

_____

Title _____

_____

Author _____

_____

What I Read About _____

_____

Title _____

_____

Author _____

_____

What I Read About _____

_____

Name _____

Listen to the sound the letters **ee**, **ea**, -**e**, and **ie** stand for.

t**ee**th   s**ea**l   **he**   p**ie**ce

Circle the word that names each picture. Then write the word.

1. sheet   she
   _____

2. peel   peek
   _____

3. bean   beak
   _____

4. weak   wheat
   _____

5. piece   peas
   _____

6. eat   eel
   _____

Name _____

pretty	says	about	give	write	were

Use the words from the box to complete the sentences.

_____

1. Here is a book _____ cats.

_____

2. "What is it?" _____ Gram.

_____

3. "Did you _____ it?" I ask.

_____

4. I _____ her the book.

_____

5. The cover is _____.

_____

6. We _____ glad we
   could read it.

Name _____

**As you read <u>Gram and Me</u>, fill in the
Character and Setting Chart.**

Setting	What the Characters Do There
1.	1.
2.	2.
3.	3.
4.	4.

How does the Character and Setting Chart help you
retell <u>Gram and Me</u>?

The **setting** is where a story takes place.
The **characters** are the people or animals in a story.

setting characters

Think about stories that you have read about a school.
Circle the people and things you would find in a school.

desk

bike

girl

book

pen

skate

animal

boy

Name _____

Good readers ask questions about the story as they read. If something is not clear go back and reread to answer your questions.

Read the story. Then answer the questions.

My mom is a carpenter. She can make many things with wood. She likes to let me help her. She teaches me about her tools. My mom asks me to get tools when she needs them. I love to help my mom!

1. How does the girl feel about her mom? How can you tell?

_____

- -

_____

2. Write a question that you have about the story.

_____

- -

_____

3. Now reread the story. Answer your question.

_____

- -

_____

4. What is a carpenter? How do you know?

_____

- -

_____

© Macmillan/McGraw-Hill

Name _____

Some words with long **e** have a silent **e** at the
end. The word **please** has the long **e** sound and
silent **e** at the end.

**Circle the long *e* word in each group that ends with
a silent *e*.**

1. leave   cookie   me

2. see   sea   piece

3. eve   she   bee

4. we   these   three

5. be   tea   cheese

6. please   pea   glee

7. flea   tree   sleeve

8. geese   he   free

A **compound word** is made up of smaller words.

ant + hill = anthill

yard	fall	boat	house

A. Put a word from the box with each word below to make a compound word. Write the compound word on the line.

1. rain _____

2. back _____

3. dog _____

4. sail _____

B. Circle the compound word. Then draw a line between the two smaller words.

5. grandmother   mother

6. bed   bedtime

7. flowerpot   flower

8. catnap   nap

9. book   storybook

© Macmillan/McGraw-Hill

Name _____

As I read, I will pay attention to my expression.

	Once upon a time, Fox had a funny dream. He
10	dreamed of grapes. Then Fox woke up fast.
18	"It's late June," said Fox. "Days are hot and
27	sunny. The grapes will be ripe. I know I can
37	find them." Fox set off across the hill. "Green
46	grapes are for me," said Fox. "I'll eat all that I
57	see." Fox had a nose for grapes. He saw lots
67	of them. They sat way up on vines on tree
77	branches in a field. Fox went after the grapes.
86	He ran faster to gain speed. Then he jumped
95	way up. But he couldn't reach them. Fox rose
104	up on his feet. But it was no use. He just
115	couldn't reach. At last Fox gave up. "This is
124	silly," Fox said. "I don't want those grapes.
132	They are not that great." 137

Comprehension Check

1. What did Fox dream about?

2. Why did Fox decide that he did not want the grapes?

	Words Read	–	Number of Errors	=	Words Correct Score
First Read		–		=	
Second Read		–		=	

Name _____

Realistic fiction stories tell about made-up events
that seem like they could really happen.

Listen to the story. Then answer the questions.

As I ride on the bus to school, my eyes are closing.
I was up too late last night playing on the computer.
Suddenly, my eyes open and I am awake. "Oh, no! I left
my homework on the table!" I think about how sad my
teacher will be. I think this might not be a good day.

1. Write to tell how the character feels at the beginning of
the story. Circle the clues in the story that help you know.

_____

- -

_____

2. What is the character's problem? Circle the best answer.
His computer is broken.
His homework is at home.

3. Write about a time when you forgot something.

_____

- -

_____

- -

_____

Name _____

A **numerical list** is a series of things written in
1, 2, 3 order.

Make two lists. Use the words below to help you.

pen	pants	tape
hat	desk	socks

Things for a Trip   **Things for School**

_____

1. _____

2. _____

3. _____

_____

1. _____

2. _____

3. _____

Draw a picture of something else you need at school.

Name _____

A **Reading Log** tells about something that you read.

Read a fiction book or a nonfiction book every day this week. Then tell about what you read.

Title _____

Author _____

What I Read About _____

Title _____

Author _____

What I Read About _____

Name _____

The long **o** vowel sound is spelled **o**, **oa**, **ow**, and **oe**.

| cold | coat | snow | doe |

| coat | toe | hold | snow | fold | toad |

Write a word from the box to name each picture.

1.

_____

_____

2.

_____

_____

3.

_____

_____

4.

_____

_____

5.

_____

_____

6.

_____

_____

| better | buy | change | difficult | move | ripe |

Use a word from the box to complete each sentence.

Did you just _____ here? We have

a _____ problem. We want to

_____ an ugly lot into a pretty lot. I have

an idea. We can use our money to _____

seeds. We can plant peppers and pick them when they are

_____. Flowers can make the garden even

_____!

As you read <u>César Chávez</u>, fill in the Retelling Chart.

Retell

How does the Retelling Chart help you understand
<u>César Chávez</u>?

Name _____

When you **retell** a selection, tell the events in
order. Use your own words.

**Look at the pictures. Write what happens in each
picture.**

 1. First, _____

 Next, _____

 Last, _____

 2. First, _____

Next, _____

 Last, _____

Good readers **ask questions** as they read. If
something is not clear, reread to answer your questions.

Read the story. Then answer the questions.

My grandma says that we must work to make the world
a better place. My grandma does this every day. She knits
blankets for babies at the hospital. I help her drop them
off. She takes her friends to the store when they can't go
alone. I help them carry the food. My grandma shows me
how I can make the world better, even when I am still little.

I. Write a question you have about the story.

_____

_____

2. Now reread the story. Write the answer to your question.

_____

_____

3. How does the child feel about her grandma? How do
you know?

_____

_____

Some words have two parts, or **syllables**. You can break a word into syllables to help you read it.

A. Put the two syllables together. Write the word on the line. Then match the word to the picture it names.

1. car   rot   _____

2. pi   lot   _____

3. bas   ket   _____

4. kick   ing   _____

B. Divide each word into syllables. Then write each syllable.

rabbit   began

_____ · _____   _____ · _____

Context clues are words that help you figure out the meaning of a new word. Context clues may be found in the same sentence or in nearby sentences.

Use the <u>underlined</u> context clues to figure out the meaning of the word in bold letters. Then match the word to its meaning. Write the correct letter on the line. Use a dictionary to check your work.

a. give what someone wants or can use   **b.** dirt

c. gather plants that are ready   **d.** plants used

e. plan for a group to do   for food

1. Our town <u>planned</u> a **project** we could <u>work</u> on <u>together</u>. ____

2. The **crops** from our <u>gardens</u> will <u>feed</u> people who are <u>hungry</u>. ____

3. These bushes **provide** the berries <u>we need</u> to make pies. ____

4. When they are <u>full</u> and <u>ripe</u>, we will **harvest** them. ____

5. The **soil** in this field is very good for <u>growing plants</u>. ____

© Macmillan/McGraw-Hill

As I read, I will pay attention to the phrasing.

	"This old lot is a mess," says Flo.
08	"I wish it were pretty."
13	Jo and Mo load trash. Flo holds the
21	bag. Flo's dad mows. The goat mows, too!
29	Flo says, "Now let's grow."
34	Flo, Jo, and Mo plant seeds all about.
42	"Please don't grow slow!" says Flo. "Go, go, go!"
51	"Give it time," says Dad.
56	See what has grown. It is so pretty! Each
65	row glows! 67

Comprehension Check

1. What do Jo and Mo do first?

2. What happens at the end of the story?

	Words Read	–	Number of Errors	=	Words Correct Score
First Read		–		=	
Second Read		–		=	

A **telephone directory** lists names, addresses, and telephone numbers.

Vann,	Jay	17 Elm Ave.	555-5436
Vann,	Max	17 Elm Ave.	555-5436
Wade,	Jake	245 Main St.	555-7401
Wade,	Lon	29 Sunset Ave.	555-4269
Wade,	May	9 Sunrise St.	555-9711

Use the directory to complete each question.

1. How many people have the last name Wade? _____

2. What is May Wade's phone number? _____

3. Where does Jake Wade live? _____

4. Who has the same address and telephone number?

_____

_____

> A **fable** is a short story that teaches a lesson. The characters in a fable are usually animals that talk.

Listen to the fable. Then answer the questions.

One day, a lion caught a mouse. The lion wanted to eat the mouse for lunch. The mouse squeaked, "Please, big lion. Do not eat me. One day, I may be able to help you!" The lion said, "You help me? That is so funny, I will let you go." "Thank you," said the mouse.

The next day, the lion was trapped in a net. He could not move. He roared. The mouse came running to help. He bit at the net until the lion was free. "Thank you, mouse," said the lion. The mouse said, "Now you can see that one small mouse can help a big lion."

1. What is the lesson of the story? Circle the best answer.

Be kind to people, and they will be kind to you.
Slow and steady wins the race.
Working together makes you better.

2. Tell about one nice thing that you have done for someone else.
_____
- -
_____

A **Reading Log** tells about something that you read.

Read a fiction book or a nonfiction book every day this week. Then tell about what you read.

_____

Title _____

Author _____

What I Read About _____

_____

Title _____

Author _____

What I Read About _____

_____

Say the words. Then listen to the **long /i/** sound.

ch**i**ld   fl**y**   h**igh**   p**ie**

Write the word that completes the sentence.

_____

- -

1. Meg's kite will _____ over the trees.

try   fly   cry

_____

- -

2. Pam will _____ her shoe.

try   tie   pie

_____

- -

3. We eat lunch together on a _____ hill.

might   high   fly

_____

- -

4. Let's wave to that plane in the _____.

my   sky   cry

_____

- -

5. The _____ can walk to his house.

mild   child   cut

Name _____

Write the letter of the word from the box that completes each sentence.

> **a.** head   **b.** never   **c.** should   **d.** ball
>
> **e.** shout   **f.** meadow   **g.** Perhaps

1. The boys and girls _____ for the team.

2. The big kite was flying high over Kim's _____.

3. Ben is _____ late for the school bus.

4. We _____ get a new bat and _____ at the shop.

5. _____ we can ride together in the green _____ today.

© Macmillan/McGraw-Hill

Name _____

As you read <u>The Kite</u>, think about the plot. Then fill in the Plot Chart.

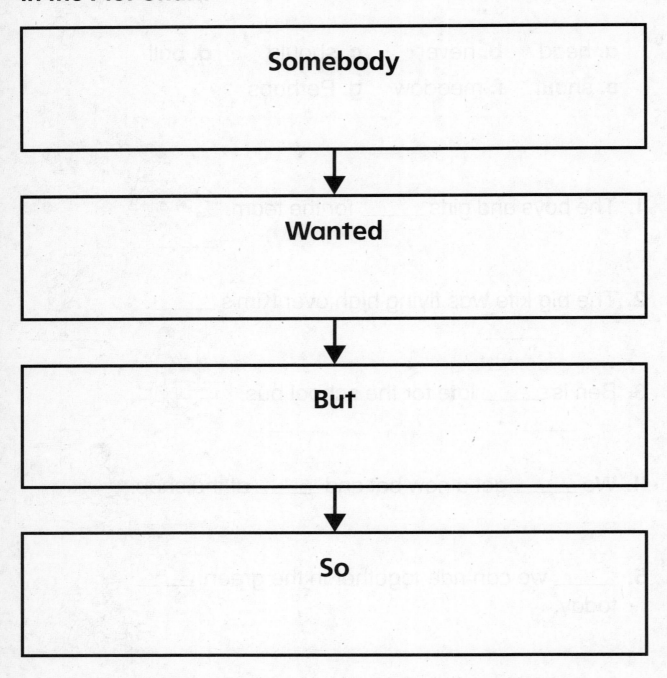

Somebody

↓

Wanted

↓

But

↓

So

How does the Plot Chart help you better understand <u>The Kite</u>?

Name _____

As you read the story about Will, think about the plot. Then answer the questions.

Will can't fly his new kite. He runs down the street with his kite. Still the kite can't fly high. Then Will takes his kite to Mike's house. The two friends try to pull the kite. But the kite just comes down again. Perhaps there is more wind on the high hill in the meadow. That is the best idea yet. Now Will's kite can fly in the wind.

1. What problem does Will have in the story?

_____

_____

2. What solution does Will try first?

_____

_____

3. What solution does Will try next?

_____

_____

4. How does the kite finally fly?

_____

_____

When you **visualize** you use the words you read to make pictures in your mind. Think about how the words help you understand how things sound, smell, look, and feel.

Read the story. Then answer the questions.

I catch the ball. I hear shouts and cheers. I smell the cold night air and the damp grass. I run with my head down. The ball is tucked under my arm. I try to run to the right. CRASH! I fly into the air. I try to sit up. I see lights and stars. My team tries to help me up. It is a good thing that I have my helmet and pads! I am okay. I still have the ball!

I. What game is the boy playing? Reread the story to look for clues and circle the best answer.

baseball   basketball   football

2. Write one thing from the story that the player

_____
-              -

hears: _____   **sees:** _____
_____   _____
-              -

smells: _____   **feels:** _____

For verbs that end with a consonant followed by **y**
change the **y** to **i** before adding **-ed**.

fry   fried

**Read the verb under each sentence. Show that the
action happened in the past. Change the *y* to *i* and
add *-ed* to the verb. Then complete the sentence.**

_____
- - - - - - - - - - - - - - - - - - - -
1. They _____ puppies at the pet store.
    spy

_____
- - - - - - - - - - - - - - - - - - - -
2. Jenny _____ her wet hand.
    dry

_____
- - - - - - - - - - - - - - - - - - - -
3. Nathan _____ to catch the bus.
    try

_____
- - - - - - - - - - - - - - - - - - - -
4. We _____ to the letter.
    reply

A verb is a word that shows action.
You can add **-ed** or **-ing** to most verbs.
A verb with an **-ed** ending means the action
happened in the past.

play + **ing** = playing

play + **ed** = played

A. Write each verb with -ing and -ed.

I. flash _____   _____

2. pull _____   _____

3. fill _____   _____

B. Use an -ing word and -ed word in sentences.

4. _____

_____

As I read, I will pay attention to the dialogue and how it affects expression.

	The bright sun is high in the sky.
08	My coach yells, "Try to win! Try, try!"
16	It's a high fly! I try to find it. The bright sun
28	blinds me.
30	"Move to the right!" yells Dwight. "Then
37	you might see better."
41	Dwight is right. The light changes. I catch
49	the fly. It's a tie. Fans go wild!
57	"Thanks, Dwight," I sigh. "You are kind."
64	"We are a team," he says. 70

Comprehension Check

1. What does the sun do to the high fly?

2. Why does Dwight say "Move to the right!"?

	Words Read	–	Number of Errors	=	Words Correct Score
First Read		–		=	
Second Read		–		=	

A **folktale** is a story that has been retold for many years. Folktales often have phrases that repeat.

Listen to the folktale. Then answer the questions.

Once upon a time, a kind old woman made a gingerbread man. After he was baked, he jumped up and ran away. He shouted, "Run, run, as fast as you can! You can't catch me! I'm the gingerbread man!" He ran past a cow. The cow tried to eat him, but he was too fast. He shouted, "Run, run, as fast as you can! You can't catch me! I'm the gingerbread man!" All at once, the gingerbread man came to a big river. What could he do? A fox came by. The fox said, "I can help you. I will give you a ride across the river. Just sit on my head!" The gingerbread man was not very smart. He jumped on the fox's head and away they swam. When they came to the middle of the river, the fox tossed the gingerbread man up, up, up in the air. And the gingerbread man did not live happily ever after.

1. Circle the phrase that you find at the beginning of most folktales and fairy tales.

Once upon a time   They lived happily ever after.

2. What does this phrase tell you? Circle the best answer.

This is a true story.   This is a made-up story.

© Macmillan/McGraw-Hill

Name _____

A **chart** gives information in an organized way.

Read the chart.

Things Frog Ate	Things Toad Ate
plums 1	peaches 2
apples 2	plums 3
grapes 8	eggs 3
eggs 2	grapes 10

Count the things Frog and Toad ate and complete the sentences.

_____

1. Frog ate _____ eggs.

_____

2. Toad ate _____ grapes.

_____

3. Frog ate _____ plum.

_____

4. Toad ate _____ peaches.

Name _____

A **Reading Log** tells about something that you read.

Read a fiction book or a nonfiction book every day this week. Then tell about what you read.

_____

Title _____

_____

Author _____

_____

What I Read About _____

_____

Title _____

_____

Author _____

_____

What I Read About _____

_____

© Macmillan/McGraw-Hill

Sometimes the letter **y** and the letters **ey** stand for the **long /e/** sound.

happ**y**   monk**ey**

**Circle the word that answers the question.
Then write the word.**

_____

1. What can you spend? _____

muddy   penny

_____

2. What can you use to lock a door? _____

money   key

_____

3. What do you call a baby dog? _____

daisy   puppy

_____

4. What can you call a rabbit? _____

bunny   easy

blue	because	until	other	also	or

Write the word that completes each sentence.

1. The team flag is _____ and white.

2. Jan is good at soccer _____ she can run fast.

3. The _____ girls run fast, _____.

4. The team may _____ may not win.

5. The girls play _____ it is dark.

Name _____

As you read <u>Animal Teams</u>, fill in the Retelling Chart.

Retell

How does the information you wrote in this Retelling Chart
help you retell <u>Animal Teams</u>?

When you **retell** a passage, you tell only the important parts.

Read the passage. Then look at it again. Underline the sentences that retell the passage.

What will we see in an ant nest?
The worker ants bring in things to eat.
Some take things to eat to the queen.
The queen does not get food.
She stays in the nest.
The queen ant lays eggs.

Draw three pictures to retell the story.

When you **visualize** you use the words you read to make pictures in your mind. Think about how the words help you understand how things sound, smell, look, and feel.

Read the story. Then answer the questions.

Today Jane is going to the shelter to pick out a new dog! Jane wants a dog that likes to play. At the shelter, there is a big room. Jane looks at the dogs for a long time. There is one dog that looks at Jane. It is a small white dog with black spots. The dog walks to Jane. It sits on Jane's feet. The dog wags its tail. Jane pets the dog. Its fur is short and soft. Jane knows that this is the dog for her.

1. What kind of dog does Jane want? Reread the story to look for clues. Circle the clues.

2. What does Jane's new dog look like?

----

3. How do you think Jane feels at the end of the story? How do you know?

Name _____

If a verb ends in a **consonant + y**, change the **y** to **i** before adding **-ed**. Do this for verbs with one syllable or two syllables.

c**ry** + ed = cr**ied**   stu**dy** + ed = stud**ied**

Write the word that completes each sentence.

1. The baby _____.

    cried   cryed

2. Han _____ his hands.

    dryed   dried

3. Kelly _____ the big bike.

    tried   tryed

4. Dad _____ the fish.

    fryed   fried

> **Context clues** are words in a sentence that help you figure out the meaning of a new word.

Use the <u>underlined</u> context clues to figure out the meaning of the word in bold letters.

1. The <u>apples</u> are **falling** <u>down</u> to the <u>ground</u>.

2. The <u>branches</u> and <u>leaves</u> <u>hide</u> <u>animals</u> in the **forest**.

3. I **heard** the <u>owl</u> <u>hoot</u>.

4. The <u>rabbit</u> <u>hopped</u> into the <u>bush</u> **before** the <u>fox</u> <u>saw it</u>.

Now match the word to its meaning:

1. falling   **a.** listened with ears

2. forest   **b.** to go from a high place to a low place

3. heard   **c.** at an earlier time

4. before   **d.** a place where trees and plants grow

As I read, I will pay attention to the dialogue and how it affects expression.

	"Piggy!" shout Bunny and Ducky. "Your home
07	is so messy and dirty!"
12	"You should never be so sloppy," says Billy. "We
21	will help you clean."
25	Bunny finds smelly jelly. Ducky finds rusty, dusty
33	cans. They toss them out. Billy wipes a muddy
42	bat. He cleans a sticky key. Piggy is happy.
51	The time flies by. "Golly!" shouts Piggy.
58	"Now my home isn't messy. I am lucky!
66	Thank you!" 68

Comprehension Check

1. Who helps Piggy clean?

2. Why is Piggy lucky?

	Words Read	–	Number of Errors	=	Words Correct Score
First Read		–		=	
Second Read		–		=	

Name _____

> A **fable** is a short story that teaches a lesson. The characters in a fable are usually animals that talk.

Listen to the fable. Then answer the questions.

Once upon a time, two frogs were friends. One frog lived in a nice, wet swamp. The other frog lived in a rut made by car wheels in the road. The rut had water only when it rained. The swamp frog tried and tried to get his friend to move to the swamp. He said, "It is safer in the swamp. There are no cars." But the road frog said, "I am used to my rut. I do not want to change." One day, a car came by while the road frog was sitting in his rut. The wheel of the car went into the rut, and the frog went flying into the air. As he landed in the swamp, he said, "You were right. It is not good to stay in a rut."

1. What is the lesson of this story? Circle the best answer.

   Be kind to others.   Change can be good.

2. What is something new that you would like to try so that you don't get stuck in a rut?

   _____

   _____

A poem often **repeats** words or sentences more than once. This gives the poem **rhythm**.

Read the poem. Then answer the questions.

The Pelican and the Fish

The fish swims.
The pelican flies over.
The fish swims.
The pelican is hungry.
The fish swims.
The pelican dives down.
The fish swims.

_____

The pelican _____

GULP!

1. Circle the sentences that repeat.

2. Complete the end of the poem.

Name _____

A **Reading Log** tells about something that you read.

Read a fiction book or a nonfiction book every day this week. Then tell about what you read.

_____

Title _____

_____

Author _____

_____

What I Read About _____

_____

Title _____

_____

Author _____

_____

What I Read About _____

_____

_____

Name _____

The letters **er**, **ir**, and **ur** stand for the same sound.

cl**er**k   b**ir**d   t**ur**n

Circle the word that names the picture. Then write the word on the line.

1.   girl
                                 gull   _____

2.   cot
                                 curl   _____

3.   fun
                                 fern   _____

4.   spurs
                                 spots   _____

5.   hid
                                 her   _____

6.   squirt
                                 squint   _____

Name _____

| full Poor another climbed through lucky leaped |

A. Write the word that completes each sentence.

1. Skunk _____ slowly
out of her den. _____

2. She was hungry. _____ Skunk!

3. Then she _____ up and saw _____ den.

4. How _____ she was! The den was
_____

_____ of things to eat!

5. A head poked _____ .

B. Write a sentence to complete the story.

_____

6. _____

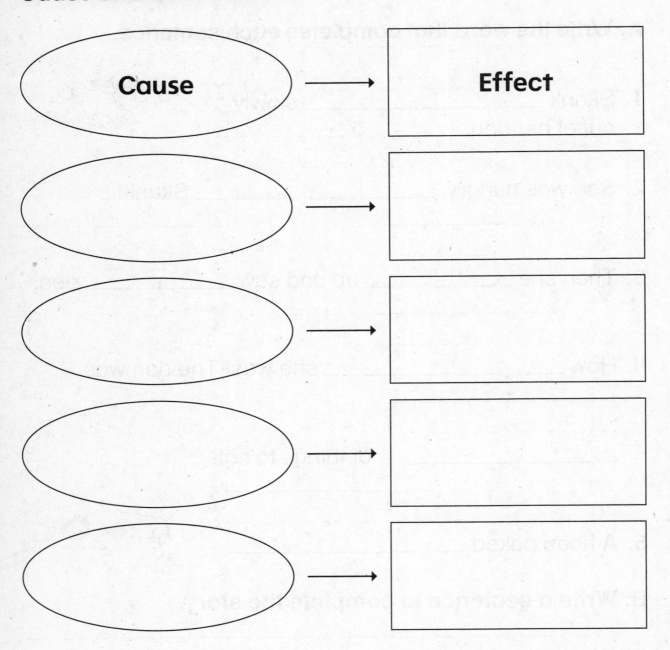

As you read <u>Kitten's First Full Moon</u>, fill in the
Cause and Effect Chart.

Cause → **Effect**

How does the information you wrote in this Cause and
Effect Chart help you retell <u>Kitten's First Full Moon</u>?

The **cause** is why something happens.
The **effect** is what happens.

cause   effect

Match the cause to the effect.

1. The dog had a bath.

2. The girl fell.

3. Bob stepped on the box.

4. The tire is flat.

5. Ben ran faster than the others.

6. It is raining.

Good readers **ask questions** about the story as they read. If they are not sure about something, they go back and reread the story to figure it out.

Read the story. Then answer the questions.

I like to look up at the sky. Today the sun is out. The sky is blue. I see white fluffy clouds. Oh, no! Now it is getting darker. The wind is getting stronger. I see a flash of lightning. I hear a rumble of thunder. I run inside. I like to watch the lightning. I count how long it takes until I hear thunder. This way I can tell if the storm is coming or going. After the storm, it is clear and it is night. I can see a full moon and the stars.

I. Write a question you have about the story.

_____

_____

2. Now reread the story. Write the answer to your question.

_____

_____

3. What does the narrator see in the sky at night?
   a plane and a shooting star
   a full moon and stars

To add **-er** or **-est** to words that end in **e**, drop the **e** and then add **-er** or **-est**.

cut**e** + **er** = cut**er**   That pup is **cuter** than this one.

cut**e** + **est** = cut**est**   The cat is the **cutest** of all.

When you add **-er** or **-est** to the end of a word, a new sound is added to the word.

Add _-er_ or _-est_ to each word. Then write the new word in the sentence.

_____

1. His pet is _____ than the wild cat.
   tame

2. The tree in the meadow is the _____.
   large

3. My dad is the _____ of all.
   brave

4. The _____ bus should stop here.
   late

Read the dictionary entries below.

middle halfway between two ends: We stood in the **middle** of the line.

mistake something thought or done incorrectly: I made one **mistake** on the spelling test.

protects to keep away from harm: The mother hen **protects** her eggs.

Use a word from the box to complete each sentence. You may use a word more than once.

1. Joan sat in the _____ of her two friends.

2. The mother cat _____ her babies.

3. Please draw a line down the _____ of the paper.

4. If you make a _____, try again.

Name _____

As I read, I will pay attention to expression.

	Miss Burns has a garden filled with herbs and flowers.
10	It makes Miss Burns smile. Her friends love the
19	garden, too.
21	Miss Burns is up early today because it is her birthday!
32	"It's my seventy-third!" says Miss Burns. "Who
40	will visit?"
42	Miss Burns checks her mail.
47	There is nothing in her box.
53	A blue bird chirps. Nothing else makes a peep.
62	Miss Burns picks an herb. It's green and curly.
71	She puts it in an urn. She feels a bit sad.
82	But then, lots of people came!
88	"Happy birthday!" they yelled. "We did not forget you!"
97	"You didn't!" Miss Burns cried. "I'm so glad!" 105

Comprehension Check

1. How old is Miss Burns?

2. What does the herb look like?

	Words Read	–	Number of Errors	=	Words Correct Score
First Read		–		=	
Second Read		–		=	

© Macmillan/McGraw-Hill

> **Nonfiction** gives facts and information about a topic. It deals with a real-life subject.

Listen to the passage. Then answer the questions.

Have you ever looked up in the sky at night and seen a flash of light? You might think that it is a shooting star. In fact, shooting stars are not stars at all! You are seeing a *meteor.* Bits of dust and rocks from space fall toward Earth. When these bits get close, they hit the air around Earth. This makes the bits of dust and rock catch on fire. The burning bits are called meteors. The meteors leave a trail of light as they burn. This looks like a shooting star. The next time you see a shooting star, remember that it's not a shooting star, it's a meteor!

I. Put the events of a meteor in order by writing 1, 2, and 3.

_____ The meteors leave a trail of light.

_____ Bits of dust and rock from space hit the air around Earth and catch on fire.

_____ Bits of dust and rock from space fall toward Earth.

2. What is the main idea of this story? Circle the best answer.

Shooting stars are really meteors.
Shooting stars make pictures in the sky.

3. Circle one important fact that you learned about meteors.

Captions tell you facts about a photo or picture.

Read the captions. Then answer the questions.

On May 28, Paul and
Mom paint his bedroom.

_____

1. Who is in the picture? _____

_____

2. What are they doing? _____

_____

3. What is the date? _____

On June 10, Pam and
Joy make a sand castle
at the beach.

_____

4. Who are the children? _____

_____

5. What are the children doing? _____

_____

6. What is the date? _____

A **Reading Log** tells about something that you read.

Read a fiction book or a nonfiction book every day this week. Then tell about what you read.

_____

Title _____

_____

Author _____

_____

What I Read About _____

_____

Title _____

_____

Author _____

_____

What I Read About _____

_____

Name _____

Together the letters **a** and **r** stand for the sound you hear in **car**. Listen for the **ar** sound in the word.

car

Read the sentence. Then write the word that completes the sentence.

_____

1. We can play in the _____.

yard

yarn

_____

2. The _____ is far away.

smart

star

_____

3. The _____ has many teeth.

start

shark

_____

4. Wheat grows on a _____.

farm

barn

_____

5. A _____ is a fish.

cart

carp

_____

6. Nana gave me a blue _____.

scar

scarf

Read each sentence. Choose the word that completes the sentence. Circle the word.

I. Dan _____ like to play.

would   house

2. The number of balls _____.

grew   knew

3. Jean said she could _____ far.

run   curious

4. "I _____ you were it!" she said.

knew   kind

5. Mike likes to look. He is _____.

friends   curious

6. Dean has another _____.

idea   knew

7. "I'm so glad we went to Dean's _____," said Mike.

friends   house

Name _____

**As you read <u>Meet Ben Franklin</u>, fill in the
Inference Chart.**

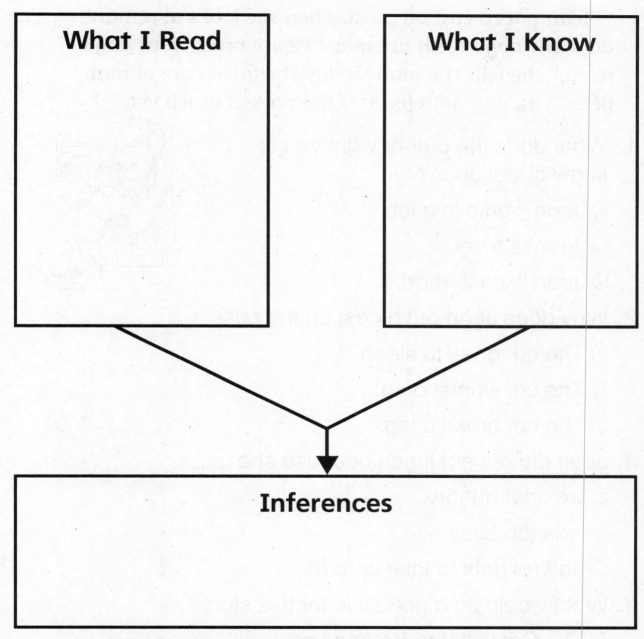

What I Read	What I Know

Inferences

How does the Inference Chart help you identify
important details in <u>Meet Ben Franklin</u> and make
inferences about them?

Read the story. Then choose an answer to complete each sentence.

Jean puts a cast on a cat. Then she looks at a man's dog. The dog's teeth are bad. "Please brush your dog's teeth," she tells the man. Today she takes care of many pets. "Oh, no!" says Jean. "I did not eat lunch yet."

1. What does the author want you to know about Jean?
   ○ Jean works in a lab.
   ○ Jean is a vet.
   ○ Jean likes to read.

2. Why does Jean put a cast on the cat?
   ○ The cat goes to sleep.
   ○ The cat wants to eat.
   ○ The cat broke a leg.

3. Jean did not eat lunch because she _____.
   ○ was not hungry
   ○ was too busy
   ○ had no pets to take care of

4. What would be a good title for this story?
   ○ The Cat with the Broken Leg
   ○ A Busy Day for Jean
   ○ The Fast Dog

© Macmillan/McGraw-Hill

Good readers **ask questions** about the story as they read. If they are not sure about something, they go back and reread the story to figure it out.

Read the story. Then answer the questions.

My name is Dr. Parker. I am a scientist. I work in a lab in a hospital. I use a microscope every day. A microscope is a good tool for a scientist. It makes very small things look much bigger. This helps me find out what is going on inside someone's body. I am like a detective for your body!

I. Write a question you have about the story.

_____

_____

2. Now reread the story. Write the answer to your question.

_____

_____

3. Dr. Parker uses a microscope to _____. Reread the story to find this information. Circle the best answer.

make small holes in the dirt
make dinner for his family
make small things look bigger

Name _____

An **abbreviation** is a short form of writing a longer word.

Look at these abbreviations.

Mister → Mr.   Mistress → Mrs.   Doctor → Dr.

A. Write the abbreviations for each word.

1. Doctor _____

2. Mistress _____

3. Mister _____

B. Read each sentence. Then circle the word that matches each abbreviation.

4. I will make a cake for <u>Mrs.</u> Smith.

   Melissa   Mistress   Miss

5. <u>Dr.</u> Shin helps me when I'm sick.

   Doctor   Mistress   Mister

6. We sent mail to <u>Mr.</u> Lee.

   Doctor   Saturday   Mister

Name _____

> A verb is a word that shows action. When a verb has the ending **-ed**, the action happened in the past. The **-ing** ending means the action is happening now. You can pick out the word parts of a verb to figure out its meaning.

Underline each word that has a word ending. Circle the base word. Write <u>now</u> if the action is happening now. Write <u>past</u> if the action happened in the past.

1. I am playing with my best friend. _____

2. My cat climbed up the tree. _____

3. Dad milked a cow. _____

4. I am packing for my trip. _____

5. We watched a good game. _____

With a partner, find 7 nouns in the sentences.

As I read, I will pay attention to my rate.

	My name is Carly. I'm a smart kid.
8	But I do NOT like the dark.
15	I know it will never harm me.
22	But I do NOT like the dark.
29	I try to sleep in the dark.
36	Mom says that I should. But it's so hard!
45	I do NOT like the dark.
51	Poor me! When I lay my head down,
59	I start to see shapes. I shout, "MOM!"
67	Mom says that the dark can play tricks!
75	It's just car lights shining on a scarf and a ball.
86	Still, it's hard to sleep. "I have a plan," Mom tells me.
98	Mom got me a night-light. She's so smart!
107	Now I can sleep through the night!
114	I am braver than ever before. 120

Comprehension Check

1. What happens when Carly lies down in the dark?

2. What does Mom do to help Carly?

	Words Read	–	Number of Errors	=	Words Correct Score
First Read		–		=	
Second Read		–		=	

© Macmillan/McGraw-Hill

A **biography** tells the true story of a real person's life written by someone else.

Listen to the biography. Then answer the questions.

Isaac Newton was born long ago in England. He was a scientist and an inventor. He invented a telescope with a mirror to look at stars far away. He also thought about gravity. Gravity is the reason things fall down. It is also why we don't float off into space! Isaac Newton had so many new ideas that the queen of England made him a knight!

1. Circle the main idea of this biography.
   Isaac Newton was a scientist.
   The life of Isaac Newton.

2. Circle one fact you learned about Isaac Newton.

3. Put the events in order. Write 1, 2, and 3 on the lines.

   _____ The queen of England made Isaac Newton a knight.

   _____ Isaac Newton was born in England.

   _____ Isaac Newton was a scientist.

4. Is this story of Isaac Newton true or a fantasy? How can you tell?

   _____

   _____

Bold print points out important words.

Read the story. Then write the answer to each question below.

Ben Franklin was an **inventor**. He came up with ideas for many things that would help to make people's lives better. His **Franklin Stove** was a much safer way for people to burn wood for heat and for cooking. Even now we use a **lightning rod** to protect houses and ships from lightning. He gave his inventions away for **free**.

1. What is an inventor?

_____

\- -

_____

2. What did people use as a safer way to burn wood?

_____

\- -

_____

3. What does a lightning rod do?

_____

\- -

_____

A **Reading Log** tells about something that you read.

Read a fiction book or a nonfiction book every day this week. Then tell about what you read.

_____

Title _____

_____

Author _____

_____

What I Read About _____

_____

Title _____

_____

Author _____

_____

What I Read About _____

_____

The letters **or**, **oar**, and **ore** can stand for the middle sound in **horse**.

**Circle the word that completes the sentence.
Then write the word on the line.**

1. The _____ is in the barn.

    porch   horse   roar

2. The _____ is sharp.

    storm   stork   thorn

3. They found _____ in the mine.

    ore   store   floor

4. The lamp has a new _____.

    cord   fork   soar

Name _____

A. Use words in the box to complete the sentences.

Their	cold	warm	great	know

1. A hat helps keep you _____ in the winter.

2. Ice is very _____.

3. We had a _____ time at the party.

4. _____ dog is black and white.

5. I _____ how to tie my shoes.

B. Match the word to its meaning.

6. sound   very great; dangerous

7. predict   something you hear

8. extreme   to guess what will happen next

© Macmillan/McGraw-Hill

Name _____

As you read Stormy Weather, fill in the Compare and Contrast Chart.

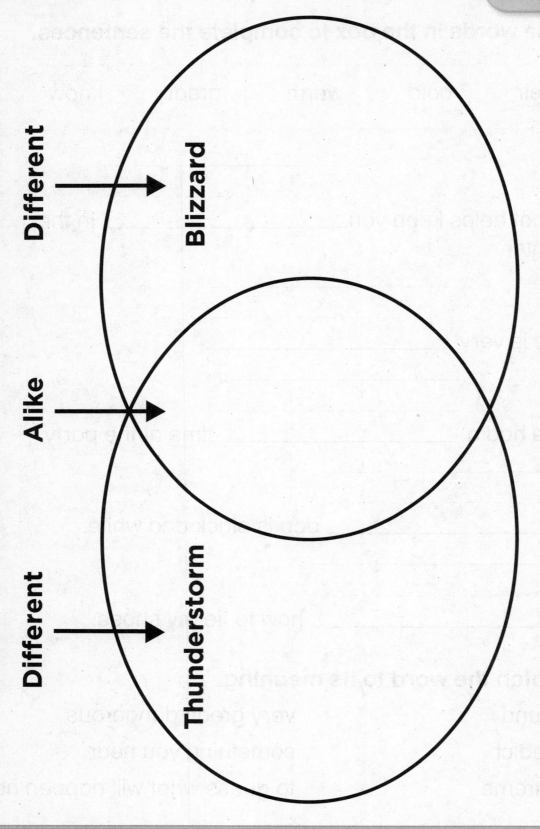

Different → Blizzard

Alike →

Different → Thunderstorm

How does the Compare and Contrast Chart help you better understand Stormy Weather?

© Macmillan/McGraw-Hill

Name _____

When you **compare** two things, you see how they are the same.

When you **contrast** two things, you see how they are different.

Jay and May both like the water.
When it is warm, they go swimming.
When it is cool, Jay runs with a kite.
May digs holes.
If it rains, Jay takes a nap and May
has a snack.
When the weather is extreme, they both go home.

Compare Jay and May by listing how they are the same.

_____
- -
_____

Contrast Jay and May by telling how they are different.

_____
- -
_____
_____
- -
_____

> Good readers **ask questions** about the story as
> they read. If they are not sure about something,
> they go back and reread the story to figure it out.

Read the story. Then answer the questions.

Where I live, people say, "If you don't like the weather,
wait five minutes." Yesterday, it was warm and sunny. I
wore shorts and a T-shirt. My mom took us to the park.
We rode our bikes. After dinner, we had a big storm. We
saw lightning and thunder. The storm also made the
weather change. It turned much colder. No more shorts!

I. Write a question you have about the story.

_____

_____

2. Now reread the story. Write the answer to your question.

_____

_____

3. What does the saying "If you don't like the weather, wait
five minutes" mean? Circle the best answer.

If it is a nice day, you should go to the park.

The weather here changes a lot.

Name _____

The letters **ea** can stand for the short **e** sound.

br**ea**d

Circle the word in each group that has the short *e* sound. Then write the word.

1. head   peach   bear   _____

2. beach   spread   fear   _____

3. bead   thread   deal   _____

4. leaf   feast   sweat   _____

5. weather   sea   each   _____

6. neat   heavy   peanut   _____

Words with the same or almost the same meaning are **synonyms**. You can use a **dictionary** or a **thesaurus** to find synonyms. A thesaurus is a book that lists synonyms.

build to make something: Tim will **build** a house.

Synonyms: construct, make, create, form, and put together: Tim will **construct** a house.

Circle the two synonyms in each row that could complete the sentence.

1. That inventor has a clever _____.

broken   invention   creation

2. The robot can _____.

speak   paper   talk

3. The robot won the _____ in the contest.

prize   box   award

As I read, I will pay attention to phrasing.

	Mort is smaller than most of the children in
09	his class. So Mort's pal Cory named him Mort
18	the Short. Mort isn't good at running or other sports.
28	But he tries hard. He runs until he is worn out. His
40	mom yells, "Stop, Mort!"
44	At school, Miss Gore said, "We will have a Math
54	Bee." Mort's heart soared. He knew that he would win.
64	Mort did his math from morning until night. He added
74	up the numbers that his mom named. He got each
84	sum right!
86	But Cory gave Mort a hard time. "You won't win,"
96	she said. "I'm better at math than you are." That made
107	Mort study more than before! The Math Bee came.
116	Cory did well, but Mort got the Grand Prize! The class
127	roared. The prize was a big, round pin. Cory said, "Now I'll
139	have to name you Mort the Math Whiz!" 147

Comprehension Check

1. What made Mort feel happy?

2. Why did Cory give Mort the name Mort the Math Whiz?

	Words Read	−	Number of Errors	=	Words Correct Score
First Read		−		=	
Second Read		−		=	

The **title** of a book is the name of the book. The **author** of a book writes the story. The **illustrator** makes the pictures. A **table of contents** tells what is inside the book.

Table of Contents
Sam's Big Day 7
Nan Needs Help 14
Nan and Sam's New Friends . . . 27

**Look at the book cover and the Table of Contents.
Then answer the questions.**

1. Who wrote the book? _____

2. What is the title of the book? _____

3. Who made the pictures? _____

4. On what page would you read about Sam's Big Day? _____

A **poem** often uses words that start with the same sound or words that rhyme. Poems try to use interesting words to paint a picture of something in the reader's mind.

Listen to the poem. Then answer the questions.

I love it when it's cold and gray.
That is my favorite kind of day.
The wind, it howls, and the rain, it falls.
The hail comes down like bouncing balls.
I can curl up with a book to read.
A cup of cocoa is all I need.
I feel safe and cozy in my bed like a nest.
A cold rainy day is really the best.

1. Circle the words that rhyme.

2. Complete the rhyming lines below to make your own weather poem.

_____

- -

On a _____ day,

_____

- - - - - - - - - - - - - - - - - - -

_____ is what I like to play.

Name _____

A **Reading Log** tells about something that you read.

Read a fiction book or a nonfiction book every day this week. Then tell about what you read.

_____

Title _____

_____

Author _____

_____

What I Read About _____

_____

Title _____

_____

Author _____

_____

What I Read About _____

_____

Use words from the box to complete the sentences.

cow	mouse	crown	clown
out	round	shout	

1. The king had a gold _____ on his head.

2. The ball was red and _____.

3. We can't go _____ to play if it is raining.

4. The cat ran after the little _____.

5. "Don't _____ at me," yelled Ben.

6. The brown _____ lives on a farm.

7. The funny _____ had a red nose and big feet.

Use the words from the box to complete the story.

against	fall	sure	below
yellow	orange	wondered	season

1. Look! Summer is gone. It is _____.

2. It is the best _____ of the year.

3. I am _____ this will be a nice fall.

4. Leaves turn red, orange, and _____.

5. I like the _____ leaves better than the red or yellow ones.

6. She _____ why the leaves fell.

As you read <u>Happy Fall!</u>, fill in the Sequence Chart.

First

↓

Next

↓

Then

↓

Last

How does the Sequence Chart help you visualize what happens in <u>Happy Fall!</u>?

The **sequence** tells what happens **first**, **next**, **then**, and **last** in story order.

Look at the pictures. Write what happens in each picture.

 1. First, _____.

 2. Next, _____.

 3. Then, _____.

 4. Last, _____.

When you **summarize**, you retell the most important parts of a story in your own words.

Read the story. Then answer the questions.

This fall, we went to see my cousins in Vermont. We had to take an airplane to get there. It was very far away. We had fun while we were there. We hiked in the mountains. We found pretty leaves that were red, orange, brown, and yellow. We visited a maple syrup farm. We sure had a great time with our cousins. We were sad when it was time to go, but we know that they will come visit us soon. We can't wait to show them our part of Texas!

1. What would you show people who came to visit you?

   _____

   _____

2. Draw or write what happened in the beginning, middle, and end of the story.

   beginning   middle   end

Name _____

Some words end with a silent **e**. The **e** in these
words does not make a sound.

A. Circle the word that names each picture.

1.   moose   mound

2.   chick   cheese

3.   house   horn

4.   horse   help

**B. Use words from the box to complete each
sentence. Write the word on the line.**

| please | blouse | choose | noise |

5. It is kind to say _____ and thank you.

6. A lot of _____ can hurt your ears.

A **base word** is the word part that is left when you remove the **inflectional ending -ed** or **-ing**. You can use the base word to figure out the meaning of a word.

The teacher is **forming** the clay.
The base word is **form**.
  Form means to give shape to something.

Write the base word.

1. moved   moving   _____

2. listening   listened   _____

3. crashed   crashing   _____

4. whistled   whistling   _____

5. baked   baking   _____

Name _____

As I read, I will pay attention to questions in the passage and how they affect expression.

	A little brown ant had a very big family. The ants seemed the
13	same, but the little brown ant was just a bit smaller than the rest.
27	When it gets cold in most places, ants gather food to be ready
40	for the winter. So all the ants set out fast! The little brown ant
54	was left alone. "Wait for me," she shouted. But no one heard a
67	sound. When the little brown ant met up with the rest, they were
80	already on their way home. The little brown ant frowned. "All the
92	food is gone now. How will I eat?" The ant sat down to rest. She
107	saw something on the ground. The ant got closer. "Great!" she
118	cried loudly. "It's a big, beautiful hunk of sweet cake. How will I
131	get it home from here? I am much too small." The ant asked the
145	animals she met for help. Each one told her, "No. I will not
158	help." "Well," pouted the ant, "then I'll have to do it myself!"
170	Crouching down, she lifted the cake up onto her head. Step by
182	step, the ant made it home! The cake would last all winter.
194	The ant had never felt so proud. 201

Comprehension Check

1. What did the little brown ant need for the winter?

2. Why did the little brown ant feel proud?

	Words Read	–	Number of Errors	=	Words Correct Score
First Read		–		=	
Second Read		–		=	

A **biography** tells the true story of a real person's life written by another person.

Listen to the story. Then answer the questions.

Can you picture a snowflake in your mind? Then you should thank Wilson Bentley. He was the first man to take a picture of a snowflake. Wilson Bentley was born on a farm in 1865. When he was young, his mother gave him a microscope. He tried to use it to look at snowflakes, but they kept melting! He knew that he would have to take a picture. He tried and tried to take a picture, and after two years, he did it! The pictures helped him learn things about snow. He learned that every snowflake is different. In 1931, a book of his snowflake pictures was made. After that, people called Bentley "The Snowflake Man" because he loved to look at the snow.

1. Circle the main idea of this biography.
   Wilson Bentley did not like the winter.
   Wilson Bentley loved to study snow.

2. Circle one fact that you learned about Wilson Bentley.

3. Work with a partner. Tell what happened first, next, and last in Wilson Bentley's life.

Look at the diagram of a fire truck. Use the words from the box to complete the diagram. Write the words of the correct labels.

ladder	light	hose	cab

1. _____

2. _____

3. _____

4. _____

Name _____

A **Reading Log** tells about something that you read.

Read a fiction book or a nonfiction book every day this week. Then tell about what you read.

_____
- -

Title _____

- -

Author _____

_____
- -

What I Read About _____

_____
- -

Title _____

- -

Author _____

_____
- -

What I Read About _____

_____
- -

_____

Read the words. The letters **oy** and **oi** stand for the vowel sounds in b**oy** and b**oi**l.

b**oy**   b**oi**l

Read each sentence. Then complete the word by adding <u>oi</u> or <u>oy</u>.

1. The little child cried with j_____ at the sight of the playful pups.

2. We will need more s_____l for the new plants.

3. The little b_____ laughed and ran toward his father.

4. Jen's new t_____ toppled off the table and broke.

5. Mom has to put _____l in her car.

6. The water for our tea will b_____l soon.

© Macmillan/McGraw-Hill

Name _____

Choose a word from the box to finish each sentence. Then write the word on the line.

wild　learn　enough　air　cub　eyes　open

_____

- -

1. The tiger _____ has a sister.

_____

- -

2. Soon the cubs will be old _____ to hunt

   in the _____.

_____

- -

3. They will _____ from their mother.

_____

- -

4. They like the night _____.

_____

- -

5. Their _____ see well at night.

_____

- -

6. The cubs _____ their mouths and yawn.

© Macmillan/McGraw-Hill

As you read <u>A Tiger Cub Grows Up</u>, fill in the Sequence Chart.

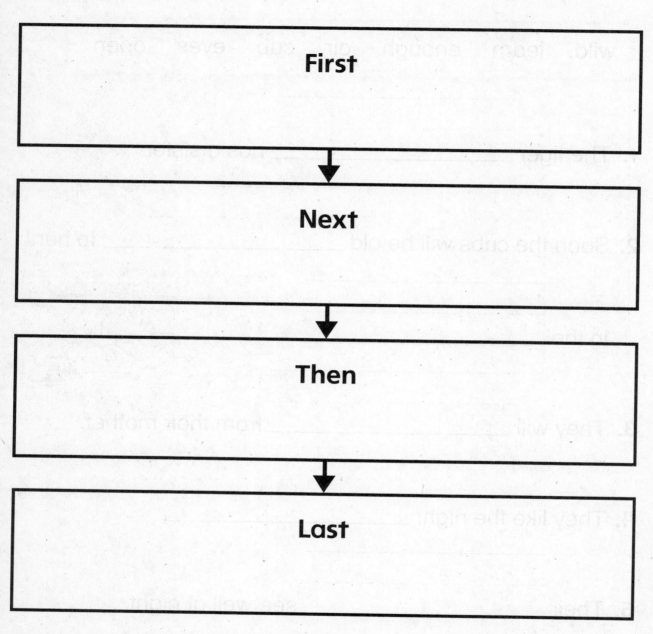

First

Next

Then

Last

How does the Sequence Chart help you better understand the order of events in <u>A Tiger Cub Grows Up</u>?

The **sequence** tells what happens **first**, **next**, **then**, and **last** in a text.

Read the passage below. Then fill in the circle of the sentence that answers each question below.

When puppies are born, they are small. Their eyes stay closed, so they can't see. Their mother feeds them milk. When they are four weeks old, puppies open their eyes and can see. They also grow their teeth and learn to stand and walk. Next, they learn how to play. By the time they are 12 weeks old, puppies are ready to leave their mother. That's when they are ready to find a new home with you!

1. What happens first to puppies?

○ Puppies are born.

○ Puppies begin to open their eyes.

2. What happens next after puppies learn to walk?

○ Puppies grow their teeth.

○ Puppies learn how to play.

© Macmillan/McGraw-Hill

When you **summarize**, you retell the most important parts of a story in your own words.

Read the story. Then answer the questions.

A frog has many changes in its life. First, a mother frog lays soft round eggs in the water. The eggs stick together. Then the eggs hatch. Tadpoles come out. A tadpole has a head, a body, and a tail. Next, the tadpole begins to lose its tail. It grows legs in the front and back. Last, the tadpole becomes a frog. The frog lives both on land and in water. It will eat worms and insects. Some day the frog may lay eggs. What do you think will swim out?

1. Put the events of a frog's life in order. Write 1, 2, and 3.

   _____   _____   _____

   - - - - - - - - - -   - - - - - - - - - -   - - - - - - - - - -

   _____ tadpole _____ frog _____ egg

2. What is the topic of this story? Circle the answer.
   fish   frogs

3. What is the main idea of the story?
   A frog eats worms and insects.
   A frog has many changes in its life.

4. Why do you think the author wrote this story?
   to teach you about something funny
   to teach you about something in real life

A **prefix** is a word part you can add to the beginning of a base word to change the meaning of the word.

The prefix **re-** means **again**: re + pack = **re**pack

The prefix **un-** means **not** or **the opposite**:
un + pack = **un**pack

Write the meaning of each of the following two-syllable words:

1. reuse _____

2. refill _____

3. unload _____

4. unsafe _____

5. remake _____

6. untrue _____

> **Context clues** are words that help you figure
> out the meaning of a new word. Context clues
> may be found in the same sentence or in nearby
> sentences.

**Use context clues to figure out the meaning of the
underlined word. Fill in the correct circle.**

1. The man <u>displays</u> the fruit. He wants
to set the melon on the shelf.

○ throws away

○ shows or sets out

2. Jordan likes to go places. He <u>enjoys</u>
taking the bus to the fruit stand.

○ likes

○ twists

3. Jordan's mom likes to <u>relax</u> at
the park. She likes to sit and read.

○ finish quickly

○ rest

© Macmillan/McGraw-Hill

As I read, I will pay attention to phrasing in the passage.

	Farmer Roy worked in Illinois. He had a nice house and
11	farm. Roy raised fat hogs. Roy's hogs sure made him joyful.
22	But Roy did not enjoy one thing. His hogs OINKED and
33	OINKED! The noise kept Roy up all night! So Roy sold his
45	hogs to a farmer across town.
51	"My farm has rich soil," said Roy. "I'll learn to raise corn."
63	Roy planted his yellow corn. Soon it was 10 feet high!
74	The next week it reached 30 feet!
81	Roy got rich, thanks to those noisy hogs.
89	"Oh, boy! I'm lucky," he said. "Illinois has some fine soil
100	for fine corn"! 103

Comprehension Check

1. Describe Farmer Roy's hogs.

2. How did Farmer Roy get rich?

	Words Read	–	Number of Errors	=	Words Correct Score
First Read		–		=	
Second Read		–		=	

Nonfiction gives facts and information about a topic.

Listen to the story. Then answer the questions.

The ostrich is an amazing animal. It is the biggest bird in the world. Like other birds, it has a beak and feathers and lays eggs. Unlike most other birds, the ostrich can't fly. It has two long, strong legs to help it run very fast. An ostrich begins big, too. An ostrich egg is as heavy as 24 chicken eggs! An ostrich grows to be 7 to 9 feet tall. That is taller than most people are. It has the biggest eye of any animal on land. Ostriches eat plants. They can also eat insects and small animals such as lizards. They also eat sand and small rocks to help grind up their food.

I. What would be a good title for this story? Circle the best answer.

Ostriches Live in the Desert
Ostriches Are Big, Amazing Birds
Plant-Eating and Animal-Eating Animals

2. Circle two facts that you learned about ostriches.

3. Work with a partner. Tell what you learned about first, next, and last in this passage.

© Macmillan/McGraw-Hill

Poets often use words in fun and interesting ways.
The sounds of words can help express their meaning.

Read the poem. Circle the sound words in each verse. Then write your own poem on the lines.

Bow-Wow

Bow-wow says the dog,
Mew, mew says the cat,
Grunt, grunt goes the hog,
And squeak goes the rat.

Whoo-oo says the owl,
Caw, caw says the crow,
Quack, quack says the duck,
And what cuckoos say, you know.

_____

- -

_____

- -

_____

- -

_____

- -

_____

Name _____

> A **Reading Log** tells about something that you read.

Read a fiction book or a nonfiction book every day this week. Then tell about what you read.

_____

Title _____

_____

Author _____

_____

What I Read About _____

_____

Title _____

_____

Author _____

_____

What I Read About _____

_____

Name _____

The letters **oo** can stand for two sounds. The first is the same as the middle sound in **goo**d. The second is a long **u** sound, like the middle sound in **moo**n. The long **u** sound can also be spelled in other ways.

bl**ue**   n**ew**   t**u**b**e**   s**ou**p

A. Change one letter in good to write two new words that have the same oo sound.

_____   _____

good _____   _____

B. Read the first word. Then circle another words in the line with the same long u sound.

1. **glue**   top   clue   bag

2. **threw**   flew   scarf   flower

3. **group**   jar   fence   you

4. **cube**   disk   cup   tube

5. **spoon**   food   walk   paper

mother	four	always	firm
father	love	supposed	

Use words from the box to complete the sentences.

1. My mom is my _____.

2. My dad is my _____.

3. We _____ each other.

4. We _____ help each other.

5. We have _____ cats.

6. I am _____ to be good.

7. Sometimes they are _____ with me.

As you read <u>Olivia</u>, fill in the Fantasy and Reality Chart. Use words from the story.

Reality	Fantasy
What Could Happen?	**What Could Not Happen?**

How does the Fantasy and Reality Chart help you better understand <u>Olivia</u>?

Name _____

> **Reality** is something that could be true or that could really happen.
>
> **Fantasy** is something that could not really happen.

Circle the sentences that show <u>reality</u>. Then underline the sentences that are <u>fantasy</u>.

1. A pig puts on a dress.

2. A pig paints.

3. A pig sleeps.

4. A pig goes to school.

5. A pig has a pet cat.

6. A pig sits in the mud.

7. A pig reads a book.

8. A pig has a mother.

As you read, use words to help you **visualize**, or make pictures in your mind, what you are reading about.

Read the story. Then answer the questions.

"I do not want to cook tonight," said my father. "Let's go out to eat!" We all cheered. We went to my favorite place. I love to eat Mexican food! First, we had some chips. The salsa that came with them was spicy. I drank some milk. Next, out came our meal. I had a big plate of beef tacos. I really liked the cheese. My mom had a salad. My dad had beans and rice. I love to go out to eat.

I. Reread the story. Circle the words that helped you visualize the people, places, and things.

2. Draw or write about a time when you went out to eat.

When **'s** is added to a word, it means that something belongs to that person or thing.

Circle the correct word and write it on the line.

1. This is _____ ball.

    Olivia   Olivia's

2. This is _____ shirt.

    Jan's   Jan

3. This is _____ bone.

    Perry   Perry's

4. This is the _____ milk.

    cat's   cat

5. This is _____ pencil.

    Mom   Mom's

pretends plays or makes believe: Danny **pretends** he is an astronaut.

vanished disappeared: The sun **vanished** when the clouds came out.

observes sees or notices: A scientist **observes** things under a microscope.

inspecting looking at carefully: Mom is **inspecting** the house for dust.

Use a word from above to complete each sentence.

1. Kate thinks Matt _____ from the room!

2. She is _____ the room for clues.

3. He hides behind the toy box and _____ to be invisible.

4. Kate _____ many clues. She solves the mystery of the missing brother!

© Macmillan/McGraw-Hill

Name _____

As I read, I will pay attention to phrasing.

	Mrs. Booth's room is planning a "Let's Find Out Day."
10	We are sitting in a small group. We will tell what we
22	plan to do. Joe will bring flowers that he grew.
32	Joy will show her drawings of clouds and blue sky.
42	I'll bring my new pet mouse, Sue. She is good at
53	learning to crawl in a maze. I trained her to find food.
65	The next day, I take Sue to school in a huge box.
77	But when I open the box, she is gone!
86	We check and recheck the classroom.
92	"Come on, Sue," I yell. "Don't spoil my plan."
101	The kids help me look. Our "Let's Find Out" day
111	is renamed "Let's Find Sue" day!
117	I don't think we will ever find Sue.
125	Now I see June point. June finds my mouse!
134	The day turns out fine. But now Mrs. Booth will
144	rethink the new rule. No more pets in school. 153

Comprehension Check

1. What is Sue learning to do?

2. Who finds Sue?

	Words Read	–	Number of Errors	=	Words Correct Score
First Read		–		=	
Second Read		–		=	

© Macmillan/McGraw-Hill

A **fantasy** is a story that blends make-believe things with things that could be true. In a fantasy, the characters might be animals that talk.

Think about "Hilda Must Be Dancing." Then answer the questions.

1. How do you know that this story is a fantasy?

   a. The characters are people.

   b. The characters are animals that talk.

2. Why do the other animals want Hilda to take up another hobby?

   a. The ground shakes when she dances.

   b. A crowd gathers to watch her dance.

3. Work with a partner. Tell what happened first, next, and last in "Hilda Must Be Dancing."

4. Dancing is Hilda's favorite hobby. Write a sentence about your favorite hobby.

   _____

   -

   _____

   -

   _____

A **map** is a drawing. It shows where places are.

Look at the map. Then answer the questions.

Quiet Town

1. How many houses are in Quiet Town? _____

2. How many post offices are in Quiet Town? _____

3. If you lived in house A, what street would you walk on to
_____

get to the park? _____

4. A new swingset was just put next to the school. What
would be a good symbol for the swingset? Draw your
answer next to the map.

A **Reading Log** tells about something that you read.

Read a fiction book or a nonfiction book every day this week. Then tell about what you read.

_____

Title _____

_____

Author _____

_____

What I Read About _____

_____

Title _____

_____

Author _____

_____

What I Read About _____

_____

Name _____

The letters **au**, **aw**, and **augh** stand for the vowel sound in P**au**l, p**aw**, and t**augh**t. The letter **a** in t**a**ll also makes this vowel sound.

Circle the word that answers each riddle.

1. A mouse is this size?

What is it?　　small　　big

2. I grabbed with my claw.

What did I do?　　call　　caught

3. When you are dirty, do this.

What is it?　　fix　　wash

4. I like to do this in art class.

What is it?　　draw　　drink

5. The girl on the phone did this.

What is it?　　filled　　called

Use a word from the box to complete each sentence.

early	along	suddenly	errand
nothing	thought	instead	

1. We woke up _____ this morning.

2. We did an _____ for Mom.

3. There was _____ in the rice jar.

4. Mr. Ford _____ he had no rice.

5. He gave us beans _____.

6. _____, it started to rain.

7. Mr. Ford told us to run _____.

Name _____

**As you read <u>Whistle for Willie</u>, fill in the
Inference Chart. Use words from the story.**

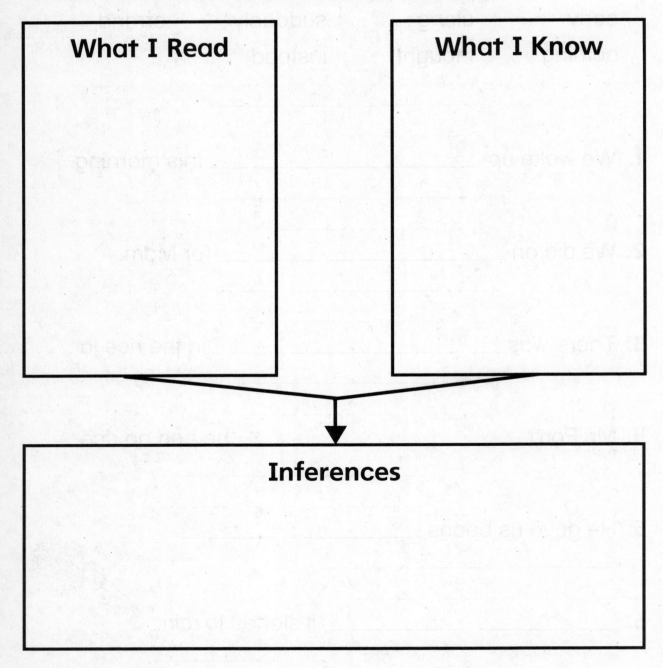

What I Read

What I Know

Inferences

How does the Inference Chart help you better
understand <u>Whistle for Willie</u>?

Look at the picture. Use what you already know. Then underline the sentence that is true.

1.

Saul likes to play ball.

Saul wins the race.

Saul likes to ride his bike.

2.

I can play catch.

I can see far away.

I can sing and dance.

3.

I can play a game.

I can help Dad.

I can read a good book.

4.

The water is fun.

The water is not deep.

The water is too cold.

5.

I don't like to help.

I can help Mom make pancakes.

I don't know how to make pancakes.

As you read, use words to help you **visualize**, or make pictures in your mind, what you are reading about.

A. Read the first part. Answer the question.

It was a rainy day. I was very bored. Mom said she had an idea. She wanted to make ants on a log for us to eat. "Ants? Yuck!" I said. But Mom said it was a cool treat.

1. Draw what you think ants on a log would look like.

B. Read the rest of the story. Answer the question.

First, Mom cut some celery. The celery looked like logs. Then I spread cream cheese down the middle of each log. Last, I added raisins on top. They looked like ants! That's why this treat is called ants on a log!

2. Look at the picture you drew. Was the treat what you had pictured? Why or why not?

_____

- -

_____

© Macmillan/McGraw-Hill

Name _____

Some pronouns go before a noun. Some stand alone.

This is **my** book. That pen is **mine**.

Use a pronoun from the box to complete the sentences. Use the underlined words as clues.

my	mine	your	her	hers	yours

1. This flute belongs to <u>Patty</u>. This flute is _____.

2. That kite belongs to <u>me</u>. That kite is _____.

3. This is <u>Lisa's</u> pet. This is _____ pet.

4. This kitten belongs to <u>you</u>. This kitten is

_____

_____.

> **Context clues** are words that help you figure out the meaning of a new word. Context clues may be found in the same sentence or in nearby sentences.

Fill in the circle next to the correct meaning of the bold word. Use the <u>underlined</u> context clues to figure out the meaning of each word.

1. The girls are <u>giggling</u> and **fooling** around on the stage.

   ○ acting silly   ○ cleaning

2. They are in a show about <u>stars</u> and <u>planets</u> in **space**.

   ○ the beach   ○ a place where astronauts travel

3. The big **helmet** <u>hides</u> most of Seta's <u>face</u>.

   ○ boots   ○ something that protects a person's head

4. Maria <u>fell</u> <u>down</u>. Her moon rocks **tumbled** <u>off</u> the <u>stage</u>.

   ○ dropped   ○ dug

5. "These space boots make it hard to <u>feel</u> the **earth** <u>under</u> my <u>feet</u>," said Seta.

   ○ cold water   ○ ground; also the planet where we live

As I read, I will pay attention to the phrasing.

	Dawn always played ball with Paul on the lawn.
09	One day, Paul threw the ball high
16	and Dawn caught it.
20	Then Dawn threw the small ball too hard.
28	It wasn't her fault.
32	It caused the ball to go past Paul.
40	Dawn saw it go in the street.
47	Paul ran to scoop up the ball. Dawn called,
56	"No, Paul! Don't get the ball! Stay on the lawn!"
66	Dawn ran to stop Paul. She grabbed Paul's legs
75	and stuck to him like glue.
81	Dawn made Paul fall.
85	Mother and Father ran outside.
90	"Nice job, Dawn!" Mother said. "You saved Paul!"
98	"I love Paul," said Dawn.
103	"I always want him to be safe." 110

Comprehension Check

1. What were Dawn and Paul doing?

2. How did Dawn save Paul?

	Words Read	–	Number of Errors	=	Words Correct Score
First Read		–		=	
Second Read		–		=	

Folk tales are stories that have been told for many years. They often include animals that talk and act like people.

Think about the folk tale "Turtle's Race with Beaver." Then circle the best answer to each question.

1. The folk tale begins with the words "Long ago." What does that tell you about the story?

   a. The story has been told many times.

   b. This story happens today.

2. How do you know that "Turtle's Race with Beaver" is a folk tale?

   a. The story takes place in a pond.

   b. The animals talk and act like people.

3. What lesson did Beaver learn?

   a. Never race a turtle.

   b. Always share with others.

4. The folk tale ends with Beaver living "happily through all seasons to come." What does that tell you about the story?

   a. Beaver learned a lesson and was happy.

   b. Beaver had to leave the pond but lived a long time.

Name _____

A **list** is a series of things written in a certain order.

Dogs can do these jobs:

1. look for clues

2. help the blind

3. pull a sled

4. watch sheep

Read the list. Draw a line to the answer.

1. Which dog helps the blind?

2. Which dog looks for clues?

3. Which dog watches sheep?

4. Which dog pulls a sled?

A **Reading Log** tells about something that you read.

Read a fiction book or a nonfiction book every day this week. Then tell about what you read.

_____

Title _____

_____

Author _____

_____

What I Read About _____

_____

Title _____

_____

Author _____

_____

What I Read About _____

_____

Name _____

When **re-** or **un-** is added to the beginning of a word, it changes the meaning of the word.

re- = again   **un-** = not

When **re-** or **un-** is added to the beginning of a word, the word gets another syllable.

Add <u>re-</u> or <u>un-</u> to each of the base words below. Write the words on the lines.

I. check _____ _____

2. hurt _____ _____

3. safe _____ _____

4. play _____ _____

5. read _____ _____

6. use _____ _____

7. fair _____ _____

8. heat _____ _____

Use the words in the box to complete each sentence.

| only | laugh | goes | build | ordinary | interesting |

1. People like to _____.

2. It eats _____ the leaf.

3. She _____ in.

4. This bird is _____.

5. This bird is more _____.

6. Let's watch the bird _____ a nest.

Name _____

As you read Cool Jobs, fill in the Classify and Categorize Chart. Use words from the selection.

Classify and Categorize	
Jobs to Make Things	**Jobs That Help**

How does the Classify and Categorize Chart help you better understand Cool Jobs?

Write <u>A</u> if the sentence or sentences tell how two or more things are alike. Write <u>D</u> if the sentence or sentences tell how two or more things are different.

1. Ted has a black dog. May has a black cat. _____

2. Sam likes to sing and Mike likes to dance. _____

3. Dana and Karen have on blue pants. _____

4. Cara's flowers are red. Nia's flowers are pink. _____

5. Both toys are broken. _____

6. All of the babies are small. _____

If a story is not clear as you read it, ask yourself questions about it. Then **reread** the story. Look for clues to answer your questions.

Read the story. Then answer the questions.

A Dentist's Job

A dentist helps take care of your teeth. A dentist looks for cavities in your teeth. The dentist may use an x-ray machine. The x-ray takes a picture of the inside of your teeth. A cavity will appear as a dark spot on the x-ray picture. A dentist takes care of the cavity and makes your teeth healthier. You can help a dentist by brushing and flossing your teeth twice a day. Try to brush in the morning and at night.

1. Write a question that you have about a dentist's job.

_____

- -

_____

2. Reread the story. Look for clues to answer your question.

_____

- -

_____

_____

- -

_____

The letters *air*, *are*, and *ear* can make the same sound.

ch**air**   sp**are**   p**ear**

Write the words from the box that have the same vowel sound and spelling as the name of the picture.

fair	bear	dare	wear	pair	share

1.

square

_____   _____

_____   _____

2.

stair

_____   _____

_____   _____

3.

pear

_____   _____

_____   _____

© Macmillan/McGraw-Hill

A **dictionary** is a book that gives the meaning of words. Some words have more than one meaning.

Read the definitions below.

flyer 1. a person who flies aircraft: The **flyer** did tricks in the small plane. **2.** a sheet of paper with information: The **flyer** gave the time and place of the sale.

model 1. a person who shows off clothes or other things: The **model** came down the runway in a beautiful dress. **2.** a small example of something: Jim built a ship **model**.

**Choose the correct definition for the word.
Fill in the circle.**

1. flyer ○ paper with words ○ fix a roof

2. flyer ○ place in line ○ person in a plane

3. model ○ sit down ○ show off clothes

4. model ○ small example ○ sandy beach

Use a word from above in a sentence.

_____

- -

_____

As I read, I will pay attention to phrasing.

	Some say Orville and Wilbur Wright were born to fly.
10	Their 1903 flight was the first of its kind. As children
21	the boys got along well. One night their dad came
31	home early with a present for them. He tossed it up
42	high. Did it just fall and drop? No, instead it sped
53	right by! Why? It had rubber bands to wind up. As the
65	bands unwound, the toy flew. That flying toy might
74	have started a big dream.
79	As grown-ups, the men had a real goal. They wanted
90	to make the first plane and fly it. The men worked
101	hard. Would the plane fly and return to land? Or
111	would it crash? The first test flights didn't go well. But
122	the men weren't unhappy. They still had hope. They
131	found a way to fix the problems.
138	In the winter of 1903, they got their plane to fly. What
150	a sight it was to see a plane flying like a bird! 162

Comprehension Check

1. What started Orville and Wilbur Wright's dream?
2. In what season was the first airplane flight?

	Words Read	–	Number of Errors	=	Words Correct Score
First Read		–		=	
Second Read		–		=	

© Macmillan/McGraw-Hill

Name _____

You can use the Internet to find out about a topic.
Put important words, or keywords, in the search
box. Then hit GO, and a list of links will pop up.

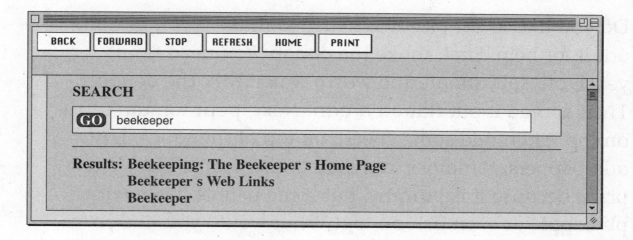

**Write the keywords you might type in the search box
to look up the following:**

1. You want to know more
about the moon.

_____
_____

2. You want to find out about
places to see in New York.

_____
_____

3. You want to know more about
the animal you like best.

_____
_____

4. You want to find out about
a job you would like.

_____
_____

Nonfiction gives information about a topic. The information the author gives is true.

Listen to the passage. Then complete the items.

Do you like to eat pizza? It's easy to make if you ask an adult for help. First, make the dough. You need flour, yeast, oil, salt, sugar, and warm water. Mix the dough. Then spread it out flat on a pan. Next, pour tomato sauce on top. Then add some cheese on top of the sauce. Last, add peppers, tomatoes, or meat. Some people like cheese pizza because it is yummy. But some people like it with pineapple or even fish on top! What would you like on your pizza?

1. What would be a good title for this story? Circle the best answer.

Pizza Tastes Good

How to Make Pizza

2. Work with a partner. Retell what happens first, next, and last when you make a pizza.

3. There are 6 things you need to make the dough. Reread the passage. Write two of the things you need below.

_____   _____

- - - - - - - - - - - - - - - - -   - - - - - - - - - - - - - - - - -

_____   _____

Name _____

A **Reading Log** tells about something that you read.

Read a fiction book or a nonfiction book every day this week. Then tell about what you read.

_____

Title _____

_____

Author _____

_____

What I Read About _____

_____

Title _____

_____

Author _____

_____

What I Read About _____

_____

Name _____

Practice

Phonics:
Two Syllable Words:
Open and Closed
Syllables

A **syllable** is a word part that has one vowel sound. Some words have more than one syllable.

A syllable that ends in a vowel is called an **open syllable**. The vowel sound is usually long.
Examples: **ti**-ger   **fro**-zen

A syllable that ends in a consonant is called a **closed syllable**. The vowel sound is usually short.

Examples: **up**-set   **vel**-vet

Read each word below. Listen for the two syllables. Write <u>O</u> if the first syllable is an <u>open</u> syllable. Write <u>C</u> if the first syllable is a <u>closed</u> syllable.

I. baby _____

2. pencil _____

3. broken _____

4. zebra _____

5. rabbit _____

6. insect _____

Name _____

Circle the word that completes each sentence. Then write the word on the line.

1. Where has the cat _____?

   done   gone

2. The girls have _____ best friends for years.   been   are

3. Let's keep _____ for the missing dog.

   sending   searching

4. We must look for _____.

   close   clues

5. I can't see it. It must be _____.

   invisible   instead

6. "I saw the keys _____ we left," said Mom.   other   before

Name _____

As you read <u>Dot and Jabber and the Big Bug Mystery</u>, fill in the Predictions Chart.

What I Predict	What Happens

How does the information you wrote in this Predictions Chart help you better understand <u>Dot and Jabber and the Big Bug Mystery</u>?

© Macmillan/McGraw-Hill

In a **prediction**, you tell what you think will happen next.

Read each story. Then complete the sentence to tell what could happen next.

1. The ship launches. It is flying to the moon. It will

_____

- -

_____.

2. The car is not clean. Mom drives to the car wash. The car will

_____

- -

_____.

3. It is a windy day. We have kites. We will

_____

- -

_____.

4. Dad brings home a bag full of food. He cooks the food. We will

_____

- -

_____.

If a story is not clear as you read it, ask yourself questions about it. Then **reread** the story. Look for clues to answer your questions.

Read the story. Then answer the questions.

Meet the Red-Eyed Tree Frog

A red-eyed tree frog is different from other frogs. It has red eyes. Its skin is bright green with blue and yellow stripes. Most frogs live in ponds, but the red-eyed tree frog lives in trees. Like other frogs, this frog eats flies and other bugs. Unlike other frogs, the red-eyed tree frog sleeps during the day. It hunts at night. Its red eyes help it see at night.

1. Write a question that you have about red-eyed tree frogs.

_____

- -

_____

2. Reread the story. Look for clues to answer your question.

_____

- -

_____

- -

_____

3. What facts did you learn about red-eyed tree frogs? Draw a circle around that part of the story.

© Macmillan/McGraw-Hill

Contractions combine two words. The **apostrophe** (')
takes the place of any missing letters.

we + will = **we'll**   I + am = **I'm**   you + have = **you've**

A. Write the contraction or the two words.

I. we + have = _____

2. he'll = _____ + _____

3. I'm = _____ + _____

4. she + will = _____

B. Use the contractions to complete the sentences.

5. _____ scratching my itch.

6. _____ be glad when spring is here.

Name _____

An **inflected verb** is a verb with an ending. When you remove the -**ing** or -**ed** ending, you are left with the base word.

inflected verb	**base word**
splash**ing**	splash
splash**ed**	splash

Write the ending. Then write the base word. The first one is done for you.

1. opened   _____ed_____   _____open_____

2. chewing   _____   _____

3. pointed   _____   _____

4. crawling   _____   _____

5. roaring   _____   _____

6. talked   _____   _____

Name _____

As I read, I will pay attention to phrasing in the story.

	Mark goes to Steph's yard to play.
07	They like the fresh air and have fun building
16	a wooden home. Mark and Steph finish.
23	Steph says, "Now we need to paint the outside."
32	"Let's begin!" Mark says.
36	Steph says, "Let's paint the outside green."
43	Mark begins to laugh. "We can't," he says.
51	"We only have blue and yellow paint."
58	"That's no problem," says Steph. "Watch this."
65	Mark stares while Steph mixes the blue
72	and yellow paint. "It's green!" Mark shouts.
79	"That's correct," says Steph.
83	"Mixing blue and yellow makes green."
89	"I never knew that!" says Mark.
95	We make a good pair! 100

Comprehension Check

1. What are Mark and Steph doing?

2. What do blue and yellow make?

	Words Read	–	Number of Errors	=	Words Correct Score
First Read		–		=	
Second Read		–		=	

A **poem** often uses words that start with the same sound or words that rhyme. Poems have interesting words that paint a picture of something in the reader's mind.

Listen to the poem.

I see an insect, and my mind starts to think:
Where does it live? Does it eat or drink?
What color is it? Is it green or blue?
Is its name Tommy, Skip, or Sue?
How many legs, and how many eyes?
How does it move? I wonder if it flies.
Does it run? Does it crawl? Can it swim or jump?
Is it long and thin or rather plump?
All of these things I wonder as I look.
I think I need my science book!

I. Circle the words that rhyme in the poem.

2. Write two more rhyming lines to complete the poem.

_____

- -

_____

- -

_____

© Macmillan/McGraw-Hill

Name _____

A **head** tells what information is in a section of an article or story.

A. Read the article about spiders.

Spiders

A spider is a small animal. A spider can be black, red, brown, or even yellow.

The Body of a Spider

A spider has 2 body parts. It also has 8 legs. An insect has only 6 legs.

The Home of a Spider

A spider lives in a web. It spins a sticky web. When a bug flies into the web, it gets stuck. Then the spider eats it.

B. Answer the questions about the article.

1. Circle the two heads that tell what information is in the sections.

2. Write one fact from each section.

_____

- -

_____

_____

- -

_____

Name _____

A **Reading Log** tells about something that you read.

Read a fiction book or a nonfiction book every day this week. Then tell about what you read.

_____

_____

Title _____

_____

Author _____

_____

What I Read About _____

_____

Title _____

_____

Author _____

_____

What I Read About _____

_____

Name _____

Practice
Phonics:
Two Syllable Words:
Final Stable
Syllables

> Some words have more than one **syllable**, or word part.

Read each sentence. Circle the word with two syllables. Write the word on the line.

1. Meg sat at the table with Dad. _____

2. The turtle has a hard shell. _____

3. The apple I like best is red. _____

4. Most clowns know how to juggle. _____

5. The horse is in the stable. _____

© Macmillan/McGraw-Hill

Name _____

straight   certain   begin   brought
minutes   around   daydream   cancel

Choose the correct word from the box and write it on the line.

1. Ann had a _____.

2. How did the dream _____?

3. A cat _____ Ann a beautiful car.

4. Ann drove the car _____ town.

5. Then she went _____ back home.

Name _____

As you read <u>Super Oscar</u>, fill in the Character and Setting Chart.

Character	Setting

How does the information you wrote in this Character and Setting Chart help you retell <u>Super Oscar</u>?

The **characters** are the people or animals in a story.

The **setting** is where the story happens.

Look at the pictures. Answer the questions about the characters and setting.

_____

1. Who is the story about? _____

_____

2. Where does the story happen? _____

3. How does the character feel at the end?

_____

_____

If a story is not clear as you read it, ask yourself questions about it. Then **reread** the story. Look for clues to answer your questions.

Read the story. Then answer the questions.

A Rainy Day in August

It's raining out, but it will still be fun because I am going to a movie downtown! I have not been to a movie in a long time. I am very excited. Dad pays for our tickets, and we go inside. Mom gives me money to get nachos with cheese sauce. Then it's time to find a good seat. Soon, the movie starts. It is so silly that is causes us to laugh out loud. I'm so glad that we can enjoy this rainy day in August together.

1. Write a question that you have about this fun day.

_____

- -

_____

2. Reread the story. Look for clues to answer your question.

_____

- -

_____

_____

- -

_____

Name _____

> A **compound word** is made up of smaller words.
>
> pop + corn = **popcorn**
>
> pea + nuts = **peanuts**
>
> Compound words have more than one syllable.

A. Match a word on the left to a word on the right to make a compound word. Then write the word.

1. pan   end   _____

2. camp   dream   _____

3.   day   cakes   _____

4.   week   ground   _____

B. Use one compound word in a sentence.

_____

5. _____

Use the <u>underlined</u> context clues to figure out the meaning of the word in bold letters. Then match the word to its meaning. Write the correct letter on the line.

a. moved round and round   **b.** came back

c. tapped gently   **d.** to keep safe

e. a bridge that can be raised and lowered

1. The royal family **returned** <u>home</u> <u>from</u> a <u>trip</u> to the countryside.   ____

2. The king, queen, and prince <u>crossed</u> <u>over</u> the **drawbridge** toward the <u>castle</u>.   ____

3. The happy queen kissed the prince and **patted** him <u>on</u> the <u>head</u>.   ____

4. <u>Water</u> from the <u>river</u> **swirled** in the <u>moat</u>.   ____

5. The <u>moat</u> and the <u>drawbridge</u> **protect** the <u>castle</u> from <u>strangers</u>.   ____

As I read, I will pay attention to phrasing in the story.

	Betty was very happy. Today was her birthday.
08	She had been planning a little party all week.
17	She had many games for her friends to play.
26	Many children came to the party.
32	"Let's play Pin the Tail on the Kitten," Betty said.
42	"I just need to get the blindfold."
49	Betty looked for the blindfold.
54	She wasn't able to find it.
60	"I don't know where it's gone," she said.
68	The children began searching, too.
73	They looked behind the couch. They looked under the rug.
83	The blindfold was missing. Then the cat came in.
92	"Look!" shouted Betty. "Kitty has it!
98	She wants to play Pin the Tail on the Kitten, too!" 109

Comprehension Check

1. What game are they trying to play?

2. Who stole the blindfold?

	Words Read	–	Number of Errors	=	Words Correct Score
First Read		–		=	
Second Read		–		=	

© Macmillan/McGraw-Hill

Name _____

A **fairy tale** is a story that has make-believe and magical events.

Listen to the story. Then answer the questions.

Once upon a time, there was a girl named Rapunzel. A mean woman trapped Rapunzel and locked her in a tall tower. The woman cast a spell on the tower so that it had no door. Over time, Rapunzel's hair grew and grew. When the woman came to visit, she would call, "Rapunzel, Rapunzel, let down your hair!" Rapunzel would let her long hair fall down. The woman would climb it like a rope. One day, a prince rode by. He saw Rapunzel, and he fell in love. The woman came to visit. The prince hid and watched how the woman got in and out of the tower. When the woman left, he came out and said, "Rapunzel, Rapunzel, let down your hair!" Rapunzel let her hair down to the prince. The prince climbed up Rapunzel's hair and saved her. And they lived happily ever after.

1. Circle the words that let you know this is a fairy tale.

2. What does the phrase "Once upon a time" mean?

_____

- -

_____

© Macmillan/McGraw-Hill

Name _____

Some poems have a **rhyming pattern**.

In some poems, the second line of a verse rhymes
with the fourth line.

A. Circle the two rhyming words in each poem.

The sun is out.

What a fine day!

Will you come out with me

And play?

You want to play ball,

But what I'd like

Is to ride round and round

On my brand new bike.

I saw a seed

Fall to the ground.

It never made

A sound.

I look up at

The sky at night,

And watch the stars

That shine so bright.

B. Think of more rhyming pairs. Write the pairs below.

1. _____   _____

2. _____   _____

© Macmillan/McGraw-Hill

A **Reading Log** tells about something that you read.

Read a fiction book or a nonfiction book every day this week. Then tell about what you read.

_____

Title _____

_____

Author _____

_____

What I Read About _____

_____

Title _____

_____

Author _____

_____

What I Read About _____

_____

_____